THE DRAGON BOOK of VERSE

COMPILED BY

W. A. C. WILKINSON M.A.

AND

N. H. WILKINSON, M.A.

WITH ILLUSTRATIONS BY
GILLIAN ALINGTON

BOOK II

OXFORD
AT THE CLARENDON PRESS

Oxford University Press, Amen House, London E.C. 4

GLASGOW NEW YORK TORONTO MELBOURNE WELLINGTON
BOMBAY CALCUTTA MADRAS KARACHI CAPE TOWN IBADAN

Geoffrey Cumberlege, Publisher to the University

THE DRAGON BOOK OF VERSE
is obtainable in the following forms:
Complete in one volume, 472 pp.
Book I, 168 pp.
Book II, 312 pp.

FIRST PUBLISHED 1935
REPRINTED (WITH CORRECTIONS) 1936
1937, 1939, 1944, 1946, 1949, 1951, 1954

PRINTED IN GREAT BRITAIN

PREFACE

THIS Anthology contains a variety of narrative and lyric poems intended to represent what is best in English poetry from Chaucer to the present day. The limitations of space (and, in some cases, difficulties of copyright) have compelled us to leave out much that is excellent but it is hoped that nothing of inferior quality has been included. We have avoided verses for 'young people' written by those who 'have good-naturedly composed poems for the young—in a technique often as inept as their sentiment'.[1] At the same time we have included a number of difficult poems, since many young readers appreciate the beauty of good poetry without fully understanding its meaning.

In the selections from Shakespeare we have avoided as far as possible the purely rhetorical and the speeches which depend on their context for their meaning, and have only chosen pieces which may be regarded as poems in themselves.

Considerations of space have caused us very unwillingly to leave out such fine passages from the Bible as 'David's Lament', 'By the Waters of Babylon', and others; but we have been consoled by the reflection that these are accessible to every one.

On the principle that the learning of poetry should be a delight and not a dreary task, we urge most strongly that long poems should not be learned verse by verse, week by week, and that very often members of a form

[1] Robert Bridges. Introduction to *The Chilswell Book of English Poetry*.

– iii –

should be allowed to choose for themselves a poem—or part of a poem—to learn by heart. They will not all choose the one with the shortest lines; if, after a few weeks, some persist in making such a choice, they had much better be allowed to do so rather than be forced into ruining what may later become a lasting delight.

For the illustrations, except that on p. 192, we are greatly indebted to Mrs. Alington. The portrait of Shakespeare on p. 192 is from a woodcut by Mr. John Farleigh, from the Droeshout engraving; it is reproduced by kind permission of Messrs. Basil Blackwell. The illustrations are intended to be decorations, not interpretations, of the poems. All boys and girls have some share in the gift of imagination; to those whose share is slight the drawings may act as a visual stimulus.

Care has been taken to provide accurate texts of the poems, and this has meant that in some cases erroneous readings which have become familiar through long use have been discarded (for example, in 'Epitaph on Charles II' and 'Lines written by Sir Walter Raleigh'). We have received much valuable assistance from Mr. C. H. Wilkinson of Worcester College, who kindly placed his knowledge and his library at our disposal, and from the readers of the University Press. We are most grateful to Mr. Frank Sidgwick and Mr. G. C. Vassall for their help; our deepest debt of gratitude is due to Mr. A. L. P. Norrington of the University Press, without whose guidance the book could not have been made.

Book I, in which there is a selection of lyric and narrative poems of a simpler kind, is intended to be introductory to Book II.

Book II is arranged as follows:

Part I contains a general collection of lyric and narrative verse arranged in chronological order of authors.

Part II contains a selection of more difficult poems. These are intended primarily for reading aloud or for private exploration by those who may like them. It is hoped that such an introduction may kindle an interest which will lead boys or girls to read collected works when they are older.

Part III contains a short selection of light verse which may be appreciated by the young.

W. A. C. W.
N. H. W.

Oxford, 1935.

ACKNOWLEDGEMENTS

FOR permission to include copyright poems we have to thank the following: Mr. Laurence Binyon and The Times Publishing Co. (for 'For the Fallen'); The Oxford University Press (for the following poems from *Shorter Poems*, by Robert Bridges: 'The Garden in September', 'There is a Hill beside the Silver Thames', 'London Snow', 'A Passer-by', and 'First Spring Morning'); Messrs. Sidgwick & Jackson, Ltd. (for 'The Soldier', by Rupert Brooke); Messrs. Macmillan & Co., Ltd. (for 'The Walrus and the Carpenter' and 'Some Hallucinations', by Lewis Carroll); Mr. G. K. Chesterton and Messrs. Burns, Oates & Washbourne (for 'Lepanto'); Mr. G. K. Chesterton and Messrs. J. M. Dent & Sons, Ltd. (for 'The Donkey'); Mr. Walter De La Mare and Messrs. Constable & Co., Ltd. (for 'The Listeners' and 'Silver'); Mr. Alban Dobson and The Oxford University Press (for 'Ballad of the Armada', by Austin Dobson); Messrs. Martin Secker, Ltd. (for 'The Dying Patriot', 'The Old Ships', 'War Song of the Saracens', 'A Ship, an Isle, a Sickle Moon', and Prologue and Epilogue from 'The Golden Journey to Samarkand', by J. E. Flecker); Mr. H. G. Dixey (for 'Cape Horn'); The Right Hon. Lord Desborough (for 'Into Battle', by the Hon. Julian Grenfell); Mr. A. P. Herbert (for 'Mullion'); Mr. Ralph Hodgson and Messrs. Macmillan & Co., Ltd. (for 'The Bells of Heaven', from *Poems*); Messrs. Elkin Mathews & Marrot, Ltd. (for 'By the Statue of King Charles at Charing Cross', by Lionel Johnson); Mrs. Kipling, Messrs. Methuen & Co., Ltd., and the Macmillan Company of Canada (for 'Recessional', from *The Five Nations*); Mrs. Kipling, Messrs. Macmillan & Co., Ltd., and the Macmillan Company of Canada (for 'The Way through the Woods', from *Rewards and Fairies*); Mr. John Masefield, Messrs. Heinemann, Ltd., and the Macmillan Company,

New York (for 'Spanish Waters', 'Laugh and be Merry', and 'The Rider at the Gate', from *Collected Poems*); Messrs. Constable & Co., Ltd. (for 'Lucifer in Starlight', by George Meredith); Mr. Frank Sidgwick (for 'Narrative Macaronic Verse'); Dr. W. R. Sorley and the Syndics of the Cambridge University Press (for 'The Song of the Ungirt Runners'); Messrs. Macmillan & Co., Ltd. (for 'The Snare', by James Stephens); Messrs. W. Heinemann, Ltd. (for Chorus from 'Atalanta in Calydon' and 'A Forsaken Garden', by A. C. Swinburne); Messrs. Macmillan & Co., Ltd. (for three poems by Lord Tennyson: 'Frater ave atque vale', 'The Revenge', and 'Crossing the Bar'); Messrs. Burns, Oates & Washbourne (for 'The Kingdom of God', 'To a Snowflake', and 'To My Godchild', by Francis Thompson); Mr. P. G. Wodehouse (for 'Good Gnus'); Dr. W. B. Yeats and Messrs. Macmillan & Co., Ltd. (for 'The Lake Isle of Innisfree', 'The Song of Wandering Aengus', and 'An Irish Airman foresees his Death').

O<small>N</small> *a poet's lips I slept*
   Dreaming like a love-adept
In the sound his breathing kept;
Nor seeks nor finds he mortal blisses,
But feeds on the aërial kisses
Of shapes that haunt thought's wildernesses.
He will watch from dawn to gloom
The lake-reflected sun illume
The yellow bees in the ivy-bloom,
Nor heed nor see, what things they be;
But from these create he can
Forms more real than living man,
Nurslings of immortality!
One of these awakened me,
And I sped to succour thee.

SHELLEY

BOOK II

PART I

THE PRIORESS

From THE PROLOGUE, THE CANTERBURY TALES

N.B. Pronounce as separate syllables *é, éd, és*.

THERE was also a Nun, a prioress,
That of her smiling was full simple and coy;[1]
Her greatest oath was but by Saint Eloy,
And she was clepéd[2] Madame Eglentine.
Full well she sang the servicé divine
Intonéd in her nose full seemlily;
And French she spake full fair and featously[3]
After the school of Stratford atté Bow,[4]
For French of Paris was to her unknow.
At meaté well y-taught was she withal:
She let no morsel from her lippés fall
Nor wet her fingers in her saucé deep.
Well could she carry a morsel and well keep[5]
Thát no drop ne fell upon her brest.
In courtesy was set full much her lest:[6]
Her over-lippé wipéd she so clean
That in her cup there was no farthing[7] seen
Of greasé when she drunken had her draught.
Full seemlily after her meat she raught,[8]
And sikerly[9] she was of great desport,

[1] quiet   [2] called   [3] well   [4] a London nunnery
[5] take care   [6] ambition   [7] spot   [8] reached (for)   [9] surely

And full pleasánt and amiable of port,
She was so charitáble and so piteóus
She wouldé weep if that she saw a mouse
Caught in a trap—if it were dead or bled.
Of smallé houndés had she, that she fed
With roasted flesh, or milk and wastel[1]-bread;
But sorely wept she if one of them were dead
Or if men smote it with a yardé[2] smart;[3]
And all was consciénce[4] and tender heart.

GEOFFREY CHAUCER

REYNARD CARRIES OFF CHANTICLEER

From THE NUN'S PRIEST'S TALE

THIS silly[5] widow and her daughters two
Hearden these hennés cry and maken woe,
And out at doorés starten they anon
And saw the Fox toward the grové gon[6]
And bare upon his back the Cock away,
And crieden 'Out! Harrow! and Wellaway!
Ha! Ha! The Fox!' and after him they ran,
And eke[7] with stavés many another man:
Ran Coll our dog, and Talbot and Garlánd,
And Malkin with a distaff in her hand;
Ran cow and calf and eke the very hoggés,
So were they feared for[8] barking of the doggés
And shouting of the men and women eke,
They runnen so, they felt their hearts would break.
They yelléden as fiendés do in hell;

[1] choicest   [2] stick   [3] sharply   [4] sensibility
[5] simple   [6] go   [7] also   [8] terrified because of

The duckés cried as if men would them quell;[1]
The geese for fearé flowen over the trees;
Out of the hivé came the swarm of bees,
So hideous was the noise, *a benedicite*![2]
Certés, he Jacké Straw and his meynée[3]
Ne maden never shoutés half so shrill
When that they woulden any Fleming kill,
As thilké[4] day was made upon the Fox!
Of brass they broughten beamés[5] and of box,
Of horn, of bone, in which they blew and poopéd,
And therewithal they shriekéd and they whoopéd
It seeméd as if heaven shouldé fall.

GEOFFREY CHAUCER

THERE IS A LADY SWEET AND KIND

THERE is a Lady sweet and kind,
    Was never face so pleased my mind;
I did but see her passing by,
And yet I love her till I die.

Her gesture, motion, and her smiles,
Her wit, her voice, my heart beguiles,
Beguiles my heart, I know not why,
And yet I love her till I die.

Cupid is wingéd and doth range,
Her country so my love doth change:
But change she earth, or change she sky,
Yet will I love her till I die.

ANONYMOUS
(Ford's Music of Sundry Kinds, 1607)

[1] kill   [2] pronounced *bensité*   [3] company   [4] that   [5] trumpets

PREPARATIONS

Yet if His Majesty, our sovereign lord,
  Should of his own accord
Friendly himself invite,
And say 'I'll be your guest to-morrow night',
How should we stir ourselves, call and command
All hands to work! 'Let no man idle stand!

'Set me fine Spanish tables in the hall;
  See they be fitted all;
Let there be room to eat
And order taken that there want no meat.
See every sconce and candlestick made bright,
That without tapers they may give a light.

'Look to the presence: are the carpets spread,
  The dazie¹ o'er the head,
The cushions in the chairs,
And all the candles lighted on the stairs?
Perfume the chambers, and in any case
Let each man give attendance in his place!'

Thus, if a king were coming, would we do;
  And 'twere good reason too;
For 'tis a duteous thing
To show all honour to an earthly king,
And after all our travail and our cost,
So he be pleased, to think no labour lost.

¹ canopy

But at the coming of the King of Heaven
All's set at six and seven;
We wallow in our sin,
Christ cannot find a chamber in the inn.
We entertain Him always like a stranger,
And, as at first, still lodge Him in the manger.

ANONYMOUS
(From a MS. at Christ Church)

FROM 'THE FAIRIE QUEENE'

A GENTLE KNIGHT was pricking on the plain,
Y-clad in mighty arms and silver shield,
Wherein old dints of deep wounds did remain,
The cruel marks of many a bloody field;
Yet arms till that time did he never wield:
His angry steed did chide his foaming bit,
As much disdaining to the curb to yield:
Full jolly knight he seem'd, and fair did sit,
As one for knightly jousts and fierce encounters fit.

But on his breast a bloody Cross he bore,
The dear remembrance of his dying Lord,
For whose sweet sake that glorious badge he wore,
And, dead as living, ever him adored:
Upon his shield the like was also scored,
For sovereign hope, which in his help he had:
Right faithful-true he was in deed and word,
But of his cheer did seem too solemn sad;
Yet nothing did he dread, but ever was y-drad.[1]

[1] dreaded

Upon a great adventure he was bond[1]
  That greatest *Gloriana* to him gave,
  That greatest Glorious Queen of Fairy lond,[2]
  To win him worship, and her grace to have,
  Which of all earthly things he most did crave;
  And ever as he rode, his heart did yearn
  To prove his puïssance in battle brave
  Upon his foe, and his new force to learn;
Upon his foe, a Dragon horrible and stern.

A lovely Lady rode him fair beside,
  Upon a lowly Ass more white than snow,
  Yet she much whiter, but the same did hide
  Under a veil, that wimpled[3] was full low,
  And over all a black stole she did throw,
  As one that inly mourn'd: so was she sad,
  And heavy sat upon her palfrey slow:
  Seeméd in heart some hidden care she had,
And by her in a line a milk-white lamb she lad.[4]

So pure an innocent as that same lamb,
  She was in life and every virtuous lore,
  And by descent from royal lineage came
  Of ancient Kings and Queens, that had of yore
  Their sceptres stretcht from East to Western shore,
  And all the world in their subjection held;
  Till that infernal fiend with foul uproar
  Forwasted all their land, and them expelled:
Whom to avenge, she had this Knight from far com-
    pelled.

EDMUND SPENSER

[1] bound   [2] land   [3] arranged in folds   [4] led

LINES SAID TO HAVE BEEN WRITTEN ON THE EVE OF HIS EXECUTION

EVEN such is Time, which takes in trust
    Our youth, our joys, and all we have,
And pays us but with age and dust,
    Which in the dark and silent grave,
When we have wandered all our ways,
Shuts up the story of our days;
    But from this earth, this grave, this dust,
    My God shall raise me up, I trust.

SIR WALTER RALEIGH

MUSIC

ORPHEUS with his lute made trees
    And the mountain tops that freeze
  Bow themselves, when he did sing:
To his music plants and flowers
Ever sprung; as sun and showers
  There had made a lasting spring.

Every thing that heard him play,
Even the billows of the sea,
  Hung their heads, and then lay by.
In sweet music is such art,
Killing care and grief of heart
  Fall asleep, or hearing, die.

From *King Henry VIII*
by WILLIAM SHAKESPEARE and JOHN FLETCHER

DIRGE FOR FIDELÉ

Fear no more the heat o' the sun,
   Nor the furious winter's rages;
Thou thy worldly task hast done,
   Home art gone, and ta'en thy wages;
Golden lads and girls all must,
As chimney-sweepers, come to dust.

Fear no more the frown o' the great,
   Thou art past the tyrant's stroke:
Care no more to clothe and eat;
   To thee the reed is as the oak:
The sceptre, learning, physic, must
All follow this, and come to dust.

Fear no more the lightning flash,
   Nor the all dreaded thunder-stone;
Fear not slander, censure rash;
   Thou hast finish'd joy and moan:
All lovers young, all lovers must
Consign to thee, and come to dust.

No exorciser harm thee!
Nor no witchcraft charm thee!
Ghost unlaid forbear thee!
Nothing ill come near thee!
Quiet consummation have;
And renownéd be thy grave.

               WILLIAM SHAKESPEARE
                (*Cymbeline*, IV. ii)

SONG

Sung by Amiens and others

UNDER the greenwood tree
Who loves to lie with me,
And turn his merry note
Unto the sweet bird's throat,
Come hither, come hither, come hither:
Here shall he see
No enemy
But winter and rough weather.

Who doth ambition shun,
And loves to live i' the sun,
Seeking the food he eats,
And pleas'd with what he gets,
Come hither, come hither, come hither:
Here shall he see
No enemy
But winter and rough weather.

WILLIAM SHAKESPEARE
(*As You Like It*, II. v)

SPRING

IT was a lover and his lass,
With a hey, and a ho, and a hey nonino,
That o'er the green corn field did pass,
In the spring time, the only pretty ring time,
When birds do sing, hey ding a ding, ding;
Sweet lovers love the spring.

Between the acres of the rye,
　　With a hey, and a ho, and a hey nonino,
These pretty country folks would lie,
　　In the spring time, &c.

This carol they began that hour,
　　With a hey, and a ho, and a hey nonino,
How that a life was but a flower
　　In the spring time, &c.

And therefore take the present time,
　　With a hey, and a ho, and a hey nonino;
For love is crownéd with the prime
　　In the spring time, &c.

WILLIAM SHAKESPEARE

(*As You Like It*, v. iii)

WAKING SONG

Sung outside Imogen's room

HARK! hark! the lark at heaven's gate sings,
　　And Phoebus 'gins arise,
His steeds to water at those springs
　　On chalic'd flowers that lies;
And winking Mary-buds begin to ope their golden
　　eyes:
With every thing that pretty is, my lady sweet,
　　arise:

Arise, arise!

WILLIAM SHAKESPEARE

(*Cymbeline*, ii. iii)

SONG

Sung by the Clown before the Duke

Come away, come away, death,
    And in sad cypress let me be laid;
Fly away, fly away, breath,
  I am slain by a fair cruel maid;
My shroud of white, stuck all with yew,
    O prepare it!
My part of death, no one so true
    Did share it.

Not a flower, not a flower sweet
  On my black coffin let there be strown;
Not a friend, not a friend greet
  My poor corpse, where my bones shall be thrown.
A thousand thousand sighs to save,
    Lay me O where
Sad true lover never find my grave,
    To weep there.

WILLIAM SHAKESPEARE
(*Twelfth Night*, II. iv)

HENRY V AT THE SIEGE OF HARFLEUR

ONCE more unto the breach, dear friends, once more;
Or close the wall up with our English dead!
In peace there's nothing so becomes a man
As modest stillness and humility:
But when the blast of war blows in our ears,
Then imitate the action of the tiger;
Stiffen the sinews, summon up the blood,
Disguise fair nature with hard-favour'd rage;
Then lend the eye a terrible aspéct;
Let it pry through the portage of the head

Like the brass cannon; let the brow o'erwhelm it
As fearfully as doth a galléd rock
O'erhang and jutty his confounded base,
Swill'd with the wild and wasteful ocean.
Now set the teeth and stretch the nostril wide,
Hold hard the breath, and bend up every spirit
To his full height! On, on, you noblest English!
Whose blood is fet[1] from fathers of war-proof;
Fathers that, like so many Alexanders,
Have in these parts from morn till even fought,
And sheath'd their swords for lack of argument.
Dishonour not your mothers; now attest
That those whom you call'd fathers did beget you.
Be copy now to men of grosser blood,
And teach them how to war. And you, good yeomen,
Whose limbs were made in England, show us here
The mettle of your pasture; let us swear
That you are worth your breeding; which I doubt not;
For there is none of you so mean and base
That hath not noble lustre in your eyes.
I see you stand like greyhounds in the slips,
Straining upon the start. The game's afoot:
Follow your spirit; and upon this charge
Cry 'God for Harry! England and Saint George!'

WILLIAM SHAKESPEARE (*Henry V*, III. i)

[1] fetched, derived

PROLOGUE TO 'HENRY V', ACT II

The King is preparing to invade France

Now all the youth of England are on fire,
And silken dalliance in the wardrobe lies;
Now thrive the armourers, and honour's thought
Reigns solely in the breast of every man:
They sell the pasture now to buy the horse,
Following the mirror of all Christian kings,
With wingéd heels, as English Mercuries.
For now sits Expectation in the air
And hides a sword from hilts unto the point
With crowns imperial, crowns and coronets,
Promis'd to Harry and his followers.
The French, advis'd by good intelligence
Of this most dreadful preparation,
Shake in their fear, and with pale policy
Seek to divert the English purposes.
O England! model to thy inward greatness,
Like little body with a mighty heart,
What mightst thou do, that honour would thee do,
Were all thy children kind and natural!

WILLIAM SHAKESPEARE

BEFORE AGINCOURT

Westmoreland.

O! THAT we now had here
But one ten thousand of those men in England
That do no work to-day.

King Henry.   What's he that wishes so?
My cousin Westmoreland? No, my fair cousin:
If we are mark'd to die, we are enow
To do our country loss; and if to live,
The fewer men, the greater share of honour.
God's will! I pray thee, wish not one man more.
By Jove, I am not covetous for gold,
Nor care I who doth feed upon my cost;
It yearns me not if men my garments wear;
Such outward things dwell not in my desires:
But if it be a sin to covet honour,
I am the most offending soul alive.
No, faith, my coz, wish not a man from England:
God's peace! I would not lose so great an honour
As one man more, methinks, would share from me,
For the best hope I have. O! do not wish one more:
Rather proclaim it, Westmoreland, through my host,
That he which hath no stomach to this fight,
Let him depart; his passport shall be made,
And crowns for convoy put into his purse:
We would not die in that man's company
That fears his fellowship to die with us.
This day is call'd the feast of Crispian:
He that outlives this day, and comes safe home,

Will stand a tip-toe when this day is nam'd,
And rouse him at the name of Crispian.
He that shall live this day, and see old age,
Will yearly on the vigil feast his neighbours,
And say, 'To-morrow is Saint Crispian:'
Then will he strip his sleeve and show his scars,
And say, 'These wounds I had on Crispin's day.'
Old men forget: yet all shall be forgot,
But he'll remember with advantages
What feats he did that day. Then shall our names,
Familiar in his mouth as household words,
Harry the king, Bedford and Exeter,
Warwick and Talbot, Salisbury and Gloucester,
Be in their flowing cups freshly remember'd.
This story shall the good man teach his son;
And Crispin Crispian shall ne'er go by,
From this day to the ending of the world,
But we in it shall be rememberéd;
We few, we happy few, we band of brothers;
For he to-day that sheds his blood with me
Shall be my brother; be he ne'er so vile
This day shall gentle his condition:
And gentlemen in England, now a-bed,
Shall think themselves accurs'd they were not here,
And hold their manhoods cheap whiles any speaks
That fought with us upon Saint Crispin's day.

WILLIAM SHAKESPEARE (*Henry V*, IV. iii)

JAQUÉS'S SEVEN AGES OF MAN

All the world's a stage,
And all the men and women merely players:
They have their exits and their entrances;
And one man in his time plays many parts,
His acts being seven ages. At first the infant,
Mewling and puking in the nurse's arms.
And then the whining school-boy, with his satchel
And shining morning face, creeping like snail
Unwillingly to school. And then the lover,
Sighing like furnace, with a woful ballad
Made to his mistress' eyebrow. Then a soldier,
Full of strange oaths, and bearded like the pard,
Jealous in honour, sudden and quick in quarrel,
Seeking the bubble reputation
Even in the cannon's mouth. And then the justice,
In fair round belly with good capon[1] lin'd,
With eyes severe, and beard of formal cut,
Full of wise saws and modern instances;
And so he plays his part. The sixth age shifts
Into the lean and slipper'd pantaloon,
With spectacles on nose and pouch on side,
His youthful hose well sav'd, a world too wide
For his shrunk shank; and his big manly voice,
Turning again toward childish treble, pipes
And whistles in his sound. Last scene of all,
That ends this strange eventful history,
Is second childishness and mere oblivion,
Sans teeth, sans eyes, sans taste, sans everything.

WILLIAM SHAKESPEARE (*As You Like It*, II. vii)

[1] chicken

HAMLET'S SOLILOQUY

To be, or not to be: that is the question:
  Whether 'tis nobler in the mind to suffer
The slings and arrows of outrageous fortune,
Or to take arms against a sea of troubles,
And by opposing end them? To die: to sleep;
No more; and, by a sleep to say we end
The heart-ache and the thousand natural shocks
That flesh is heir to, 'tis a consummation
Devoutly to be wish'd. To die, to sleep;
To sleep: perchance to dream: ay, there's the rub;
For in that sleep of death what dreams may come,
When we have shuffled off this mortal coil,
Must give us pause. There's the respect[1]
That makes calamity of so long life;
For who would bear the whips and scorns of time,
The oppressor's wrong, the proud man's contumely,
The pangs of dispriz'd love, the law's delay,
The insolence of office, and the spurns
That patient merit of the unworthy takes,
When he himself might his quietus make
With a bare bodkin? who would fardels[2] bear,
To grunt and sweat under a weary life,
But that the dread of something after death,
The undiscover'd country from whose bourn
No traveller returns, puzzles the will,
And makes us rather bear those ills we have
Than fly to others that we know not of?

[1] consideration   [2] burdens

Thus conscience does make cowards of us all;
And thus the native hue of resolution
Is sicklied o'er with the pale cast of thought,
And enterprises of great pith and moment
With this regard their currents turn awry,
And lose the name of action.

WILLIAM SHAKESPEARE
(Hamlet, III. i)

QUEEN MAB

Mercutio speaks:

QUEEN Mab! What's she?
    She is the fairies' midwife, and she comes
In shape no bigger than an agate-stone
On the forefinger of an alderman,
Drawn with a team of little atomies
Athwart men's noses as they lie asleep:
Her waggon-spokes made of long spinners' legs;
The cover, of the wings of grasshoppers;
The traces, of the smallest spider's web,
The collars, of the moonshine's watery beams;
Her whip, of cricket's bone; the lash, of film;
Her waggoner, a small grey-coated gnat,
Not half so big as a round little worm
Prick'd from the lazy finger of a maid;
Her chariot is an empty hazel-nut,
Made by the joiner squirrel or old grub,
Time out o' mind the fairies' coach-makers.
And in this state she gallops night by night
Through lovers' brains, and then they dream of love;
O'er courtiers' knees, that dream on curtsies straight;

O'er lawyers' fingers, who straight dream on fees;
O'er ladies' lips, who straight on kisses dream;
Which oft the angry Mab with blisters plagues,
Because their breaths with sweetmeats tainted are.
Sometimes she gallops o'er a courtier's nose,
And then dreams he of smelling out a suit;
And sometimes comes she with a tithe-pig's tail,
Tickling a parson's nose as a' lies asleep,
Then dreams he of another benefice;
Sometimes she driveth o'er a soldier's neck,
And then dreams he of cutting foreign throats,
Of breaches, ambuscadoes, Spanish blades,
Of healths five fathom deep; and then anon
Drums in his ear, at which he starts and wakes;
And, being thus frighted, swears a prayer or two,
And sleeps again.

WILLIAM SHAKESPEARE
(Romeo and Juliet, I. iv)

GAUNT'S DYING SPEECH

METHINKS I am a prophet new inspir'd,
And thus expiring do foretell of him:
His rash fierce blaze of riot cannot last,
For violent fires soon burn out themselves;
Small showers last long, but sudden storms are short;
He tires betimes that spurs too fast betimes;
With eager feeding food doth choke the feeder:
Light vanity, insatiate cormorant,
Consuming means, soon preys upon itself.

This royal throne of kings, this scepter'd isle,
This earth of majesty, this seat of Mars,
This other Eden, demi-paradise,
This fortress built by Nature for herself
Against infection and the hand of war,
This happy breed of men, this little world,
This precious stone set in the silver sea,
Which serves it in the office of a wall,
Or as a moat defensive to a house,
Against the envy of less happier lands,
This blessed plot, this earth, this realm, this England,
This nurse, this teeming womb of royal kings,
Fear'd by their breed and famous by their birth,
Renownéd for their deeds as far from home,—
For Christian service and true chivalry,—
As is the sepulchre in stubborn Jewry
Of the world's ransom, blesséd Mary's Son:
This land of such dear souls, this dear, dear land,
Dear for her reputation through the world,
Is now leas'd out,—I die pronouncing it,—
Like to a tenement, or pelting[1] farm:
England, bound in with the triumphant sea,
Whose rocky shore beats back the envious siege
Of watery Neptune, is now bound in with shame,
With inky blots, and rotten parchment bonds:
That England, that was wont to conquer others,
Hath made a shameful conquest of itself.
Ah! would the scandal vanish with my life,
How happy then were my ensuing death.

WILLIAM SHAKESPEARE (*Richard II*, II. i)

[1] paltry

MACBETH ON LADY MACBETH'S DEATH

TO-MORROW, and to-morrow, and to-morrow,
Creeps in this petty pace from day to day,
To the last syllable of recorded time;
And all our yesterdays have lighted fools
The way to dusty death. Out, out, brief candle!
Life's but a walking shadow, a poor player
That struts and frets his hour upon the stage,
And then is heard no more; it is a tale
Told by an idiot, full of sound and fury,
Signifying nothing.

WILLIAM SHAKESPEARE
(*Macbeth*, v. v)

PROSPERO'S FAREWELL TO HIS MAGIC

OUR revels now are ended. These our actors,
As I foretold you, were all spirits and
Are melted into air, into thin air:
And, like the baseless fabric of this vision,
The cloud-capp'd towers, the gorgeous palaces,
The solemn temples, the great globe itself,
Yea, all which it inherit, shall dissolve
And, like this insubstantial pageant faded,
Leave not a rack behind. We are such stuff
As dreams are made on, and our little life
Is rounded with a sleep.

WILLIAM SHAKESPEARE
(*Tempest*, iv. i)

RICHARD II'S DESPAIR

OF comfort no man speak:
Let's talk of graves, of worms, and epitaphs;
Make dust our paper, and with rainy eyes
Write sorrow on the bosom of the earth;
Let's choose executors and talk of wills:
And yet not so—for what can we bequeath
Save our deposéd bodies to the ground?
Our lands, our lives, and all are Bolingbroke's,
And nothing can we call our own but death,
And that small model of the barren earth
Which serves as paste and cover to our bones.
For God's sake, let us sit upon the ground
And tell sad stories of the death of kings:
How some have been depos'd, some slain in war,
Some haunted by the ghosts they have depos'd,
Some poison'd by their wives, some sleeping kill'd;
All murder'd: for within the hollow crown
That rounds the mortal temples of a king
Keeps Death his court, and there the antick[1] sits,
Scoffing his state and grinning at his pomp;
Allowing him a breath, a little scene,
To monarchize, be fear'd, and kill with looks,
Infusing him with self and vain conceit,
As if this flesh which walls about our life
Were brass impregnable; and humour'd thus
Comes at the last, and with a little pin
Bores through his castle wall, and farewell king!

[1] clown

– 184 –

Cover your heads, and mock not flesh and blood
With solemn reverence: throw away respect,
Tradition, form, and ceremonious duty,
For you have but mistook me all this while:
I live with bread like you, feel want,
Taste grief, need friends: subjected thus,
How can you say to me I am a king?

WILLIAM SHAKESPEARE (*Richard II*, III. ii)

EDGAR'S IMAGINARY DESCRIPTION OF DOVER CLIFF

How fearful
And dizzy 'tis to cast one's eyes so low!
The crows and choughs that wing the midway air
Show scarce so gross as beetles; half way down
Hangs one that gathers samphire,[1] dreadful trade!
Methinks he seems no bigger than his head.
The fishermen that walk upon the beach
Appear like mice, and yond tall anchoring bark
Diminish'd to her cock,[2] her cock a buoy
Almost too small for sight. The murmuring surge,
That on the unnumber'd idle pebbles chafes,
Cannot be heard so high. I'll look no more,
Lest my brain turn, and the deficient sight
Topple down headlong.

WILLIAM SHAKESPEARE (*King Lear*, IV. vi)

[1] aromatic sea-plant   [2] cock boat, dinghy

OTHELLO DESCRIBES HIS WOOING
OF DESDEMONA

HER father lov'd me; oft invited me;
Still question'd me the story of my life
From year to year, the battles, sieges, fortunes
That I have pass'd.
I ran it through, even from my boyish days
To the very moment that he bade me tell it;
Wherein I spake of most disastrous chances,
Of moving accidents by flood and field,
Of hair-breadth 'scapes i' the imminent deadly breach,
Of being taken by the insolent foe
And sold to slavery, of my redemption thence
And portance[1] in my travel's history;
Wherein of antres[2] vast and desarts idle,
Rough quarries, rocks and hills whose heads touch
    heaven,
It was my hint to speak, such was the process;
And of the Cannibals that each other eat,
The Anthropophagi, and men whose heads
Do grow beneath their shoulders. This to hear
Would Desdemona seriously incline;
But still the house-affairs would draw her thence;
Which ever as she could with haste dispatch,
She'd come again, and with a greedy ear
Devour up my discóurse. Which I observing,
Took once a pliant hour, and found good means
To draw from her a prayer of earnest heart

      [1] conduct   [2] caves

That I would all my pilgrimage dilate,
Whereof by parcels she had something heard,
But not intentively: I did consent;
And often did beguile her of her tears,
When I did speak of some distressful stroke
That my youth suffer'd. My story being done,
She gave me for my pains a world of sighs:
She swore, in faith, 'twas strange, 'twas passing strange;
'Twas pitiful, 'twas wondrous pitiful:
She wish'd she had not heard it, yet she wish'd
That heaven had made her such a man; she thank'd
    me,
And bade me, if I had a friend that lov'd her,
I should but teach him how to tell my story,
And that would woo her. Upon this hint I spake:
She lov'd me for the dangers I had pass'd,
And I lov'd her that she did pity them.
This only is the witchcraft I have us'd.

WILLIAM SHAKESPEARE
(*Othello*, I. iii)

FROM OTHELLO'S LAST SPEECH

I PRAY you, in your letters,
When you shall these unlucky deeds relate,
Speak of me as I am; nothing extenuate,
Nor set down aught in malice: then, must you speak
Of one that lov'd not wisely but too well;
Of one not easily jealous, but, being wrought,[1]
Perplex'd in the extreme; of one whose hand,

---

[1] wrought upon

Like the base Indian, threw a pearl away
Richer than all his tribe; of one whose súbdu'd eyes
Albeit unuséd to the melting mood,
Drop tears as fast as the Arabian trees
Their med'cinable gum. Set you down this;
And say besides, that in Aleppo once,
Where a malignant and a turban'd Turk
Beat a Venetian and traduc'd the state,
I took by the throat the circumciséd dog,
And smote him thus.

WILLIAM SHAKESPEARE
(*Othello*, v. ii)

WOLSEY'S FAREWELL

So farewell to the little good you bear me.
Farewell! a long farewell, to all my greatness!
This is the state of man: to-day he puts forth
The tender leaves of hopes; to-morrow blossoms,
And bears his blushing honours thick upon him;
The third day comes a frost, a killing frost;
And, when he thinks, good easy man, full surely
His greatness is a-ripening, nips his root,
And then he falls, as I do. I have ventur'd,
Like little wanton boys that swim on bladders,
This many summers in a sea of glory,
But far beyond my depth: my high-blown pride
At length broke under me, and now has left me,
Weary and old with service, to the mercy
Of a rude stream, that must for ever hide me.
Vain pomp and glory of this world, I hate ye:

I feel my heart new open'd.   O! how wretched
Is that poor man that hangs on princes' favours!
There is, betwixt that smile we would aspire to,
That sweet aspéct of princes, and their ruin,
More pangs and fears than wars or women have;
And when he falls, he falls like Lucifer,
Never to hope again.

WILLIAM SHAKESPEARE
(*Henry VIII*, III. ii)

SONNET 18

SHALL I compare thee to a summer's day?
Thou art more lovely and more temperate:
Rough winds do shake the darling buds of May,
And summer's lease hath all too short a date:
Sometime too hot the eye of heaven shines,
And often is his gold complexion dimm'd;
And every fair from fair sometime declines,
By chance, or nature's changing course untrimm'd;
But thy eternal summer shall not fade,
Nor lose possession of that fair thou ow'st,
Nor shall death brag thou wander'st in his shade,
When in eternal lines to time thou grow'st;
    So long as men can breathe, or eyes can see,
    So long lives this, and this gives life to thee.

WILLIAM SHAKESPEARE

SONNET 60

LIKE as the waves make towards the pebbled shore,
  So do our minutes hasten to their end;
Each changing place with that which goes before,
In sequent toil all forwards do contend.
Nativity, once in the main of light,
Crawls to maturity, wherewith being crown'd,
Crooked eclipses 'gainst his glory fight,
And Time that gave doth now his gift confound.
Time doth transfix the flourish set on youth
And delves the parallels in beauty's brow,
Feeds on the rarities of nature's truth,
And nothing stands but for his scythe to mow:
    And yet to times in hope my verse shall stand,
    Praising thy worth, despite his cruel hand.

WILLIAM SHAKESPEARE

SONNET 73

THAT time of year thou mayst in me behold
  When yellow leaves, or none, or few, do hang
Upon those boughs which shake against the cold,
Bare ruin'd choirs, where late the sweet birds sang.
In me thou see'st the twilight of such day
As after sunset fadeth in the west;
Which by and by black night doth take away,
Death's second self, that seals up all in rest.
In me thou see'st the glowing of such fire,
That on the ashes of his youth doth lie,
As the death-bed whereon it must expire
Consum'd with that which it was nourish'd by.
  This thou perceiv'st, which makes thy love more
      strong,
  To love that well which thou must leave ere long.

WILLIAM SHAKESPEARE

ON SHAKESPEARE

*To the memory of my beloved, the Author, Mr. William Shakespeare:
and what he hath left us*

              . . . Soul of the age!
The applause! delight! the wonder of our stage!
My Shakespeare, rise; I will not lodge thee by
   Chaucer, or Spenser, or bid Beaumont lie
A little further, to make thee a room:
   Thou art a monument, without a tomb,
And art alive still, while thy book doth live,
   And we have wits to read, and praise to give.
That I not mix thee so, my brain excuses;
   I mean with great, but disproportioned Muses,
For, if I thought my judgement were of years,
   I should commit thee surely with thy peers,
And tell, how far thou didst our Lyly outshine,
   Or sporting Kyd, or Marlowe's mighty line,
And though thou hadst small Latin, and less Greek,
   From thence to honour thee I would not seek
For names; but call forth thundering Æschylus,
   Euripides, and Sophocles to us,
Pacuvius, Accius, him of Cordova[1] dead,
   To life again, to hear thy buskin[2] tread,
And shake a stage: or, when thy socks[3] were on,
   Leave thee alone, for the comparison
Of all, that insolent Greece, or haughty Rome
   Sent forth, or since did from their ashes come.
Triumph, my Britain, thou hast one to show,

[1] Seneca   [2] boot worn by actors in Tragedy
        [3] shoes worn in Comedy

To whom all scenes[1] of Europe homage owe.
He was not of an age, but for all time!
　And all the Muses still were in their prime,
When like Apollo he came forth to warm
　Our ears, or like a Mercury to charm!
Nature herself was proud of his designs,
　And joyed to wear the dressing of his lines!
Which were so richly spun, and woven so fit,
　As, since, she will vouchsafe no other wit.

BEN JONSON

HYMN TO DIANA

QUEEN and huntress, chaste and fair,
　Now the sun is laid to sleep,
Seated in thy silver chair,
State in wonted manner keep:
　　Hesperus entreats thy light,
　　Goddess, excellently bright.

Earth, let not thy envious shade
Dare itself to interpose;
Cynthia's shining orb was made
Heaven to clear, when day did close:
　　Bless us then with wishéd sight,
　　Goddess, excellently bright.

Lay thy bow of pearl apart,
And thy crystal-shining quiver;

[1] stages

Give unto the flying hart
Space to breathe, how short soever:
    Thou that mak'st a day of night,
    Goddess, excellently bright.

BEN JONSON

FROM 'THE FAIRIES' FAREWELL'

FAREWELL rewards and Fairies,
    Good housewives now may say,
For now foul sluts in dairies
    Do fare as well as they
And though they sweep their hearths no less
    Than maids were wont to do,
Yet who of late for cleanliness
    Finds sixpence in her shoe?

Lament, lament, old Abbeys,
    The Fairies' lost command;
They did but change Priests' babies,
    But some have chang'd your land:
And all your children stol'n from thence
    Are now grown Puritans;
Who live as changelings ever since
    For love of your domains.

At morning and at evening both
    You merry were and glad,
So little care of sleep and sloth
    These pretty Ladies had;

When Tom came home from labour,
Or Cisse to milking rose,
Then merrily went their tabor,
And nimbly went their toes.

Witness those rings and roundelays
Of theirs, which yet remain,
Were footed in Queen Mary's days
On many a grassy plain;
But since of late, Elizabeth,
And later James came in,
They never danc'd on any heath
As when the time hath bin.

By which we note the Fairies
Were of the old profession;
Their songs were Ave Maries,
Their dances were procession:
But now, alas! they all are dead
Or gone beyond the seas,
Or farther for Religion fled,
Or else they take their ease.

A tell-tale in their company
They never could endure,
And who so kept not secretly
Their mirth was punisht sure;
It was a just and Christian deed
To pinch such black and blue:
O how the Common-wealth doth need
Such justices as you!

RICHARD CORBET

CALCHAS SPEAKS OVER THE BODY OF AJAX

From THE CONTENTION OF AJAX AND ULYSSES FOR THE
ARMOUR OF ACHILLES

THE glories of our blood and state
Are shadows, not substantial things,
There is no armour against Fate,
Death lays his icy hand on kings,
Sceptre and Crown
Must tumble down,
And in the dust be equal made
With the poor crooked scythe and spade.

Some men with swords may reap the field,
And plant fresh laurels where they kill,
But their strong nerves[1] at last must yield;
They tame but one another still;
Early or late
They stoop to fate,
And must give up the murmuring breath
When they, pale captives, creep to death.

The garlands wither on your brow;
Then boast no more your mighty deeds,
Upon Death's purple altar now
See where the victor-victim bleeds.
Your heads must come
To the cold tomb;
Only the actions of the just
Smell sweet, and blossom in their dust.

JAMES SHIRLEY

[1] sinews

ON THE DEATH OF MARIE, COUNTESS OF PEMBROKE

UNDERNEATH this marble herse
Lies the subject of all verse:
Sidney's sister, Pembroke's mother:
Death, ere thou hast killed another,
Fair, and learn'd, and good as she,
Time shall throw a dart at thee.

WILLIAM BROWNE

FROM 'SAMSON AGONISTES'

OCCASIONS drew me early to this city;
And, as the gates I entered with sun-rise,
The morning trumpets festival proclaim'd
Through each high street: little I had dispatch'd,
When all abroad was rumour'd that this day
Samson should be brought forth, to show the people
Proof of his mighty strength in feats and games;
I sorrow'd at his captive state, but minded
Not to be absent at that spectacle.
The building was a spacious theatre,
Half round, on two main pillars vaulted high,
With seats where all the lords, and each degree
Of sort, might sit in order to behold;
The other side was open, where the throng,
On banks and scaffolds, under sky might stand;
I, among these, aloof obscurely stood.
The feast and noon grew high, and sacrifice
Had fill'd their hearts with mirth, high cheer, and wine,

When to their sports they turn'd.   Immediately
Was Samson as a public servant brought,
In their state livery clad: before him pipes
And timbrels; on each side went arméd guards,
Both horse and foot; before him and behind,
Archers and slingers, cataphracts[1] and spears.
At sight of him the people with a shout
Rifted the air, clamouring their god with praise,
Who had made their dreadful enemy their thrall.
He, patient, but undaunted, where they led him,
Came to the place; and what was set before him,
Which without help of eye might be assay'd,
To heave, pull, draw, or break, he still perform'd
All with incredible, stupendous force;
None daring to appear antagonist.
At length, for intermission's sake, they led him
Between the pillars; he his guide requested
(For so from such as nearer stood we heard),
As over-tired, to let him lean awhile,
With both his arms, on those two massy pillars,
That to the archéd roof gave main support.
He, unsuspicious, led him; which, when Samson
Felt in his arms, with head awhile inclined,
And eyes fast fix'd, he stood, as one who pray'd,
Or some great matter in his mind revolved:
At last, with head erect, thus cried aloud:—
'Hitherto, lords, what your commands imposed
I have perform'd, as reason was, obeying,
Not without wonder or delight beheld:
Now, of my own accord, such other trial

[1] soldiers in armour

I mean to show you of my strength, yet greater,
As with amaze shall strike all who behold.'
This utter'd, straining all his nerves, he bow'd:
As with the force of winds and waters pent,
When mountains tremble, those two massy pillars
With horrible convulsion to and fro
He tugg'd, he shook, till down they came, and drew
The whole roof after them with burst of thunder
Upon the heads of all who sat beneath,
Lords, ladies, captains, counsellors, or priests,
Their choice nobility and flower, not only
Of this, but each Philistian city round,
Met from all parts to solemnize this feast.
Samson, with these immix'd, inevitably
Pull'd down the same destruction on himself;
The vulgar only 'scaped who stood without.
    O dearly bought revenge, yet glorious!
Living or dying thou hast fulfill'd
The work for which thou wast foretold
To Israel, and now liest victorious
Among thy slain, self-kill'd,
Not willingly, but tangled in the fold
Of dire necessity, whose law in death conjoin'd
Thee with thy slaughter'd foes, in number more
Than all thy life hath slain before

JOHN MILTON

ON HIS BLINDNESS

WHEN I consider how my light is spent
 Ere half my days, in this dark world and wide,
 And that one talent which is death to hide,
Lodged with me useless, though my soul more bent
To serve therewith my Maker, and present
 My true account, lest he, returning, chide;
 'Doth God exact day-labour, light denied?'
I fondly ask: but Patience, to prevent
 That murmur, soon replies, 'God doth not need
Either man's work, or his own gifts; who best
 Bear his mild yoke, they serve him best; his state
 Is kingly: thousands at his bidding speed,
And post o'er land and ocean without rest;
 They also serve who only stand and wait.'

JOHN MILTON

ON THE LATE MASSACRE IN PIEDMONT

AVENGE, O Lord, thy slaughter'd saints, whose bones
  Lie scatter'd on the Alpine mountains cold;
Even them who kept thy truth so pure of old,
When all our fathers worshipp'd stocks and stones,
Forget not: in thy book record their groans
  Who were thy sheep, and in their ancient fold
  Slain by the bloody Piedmontese, that roll'd
Mother with infant down the rocks. Their moans
  The vales redoubled to the hills, and they
To heaven. Their martyr'd blood and ashes sow
  O'er all the Italian fields, where still doth sway
The triple tyrant; that from these may grow
  A hundred fold, who, having learn'd thy way,
Early may fly the Babylonian woe.

JOHN MILTON

TO THE LORD GENERAL CROMWELL

CROMWELL, our chief of men, who, through a cloud
 Not of war only, but detractions rude,
 Guided by faith and matchless fortitude,
To peace and truth thy glorious way hast plough'd,
And on the neck of crownéd fortune proud
 Hast rear'd God's trophies, and his work pursued,
 While Darwen stream, with blood of Scots imbrued,
And Dunbar field, resounds thy praises loud,
And Worcester's laureate wreath. Yet much remains
 To conquer still; peace hath her victories
 No less renown'd than war: new foes arise,
Threatening to bind our souls with secular chains:
 Help us to save free conscience from the paw
 Of hireling wolves, whose gospel is their maw.[1]

JOHN MILTON

[1] stomach

WHY SO PALE AND WAN?

WHY so pale and wan, fond lover?
    Prithee, why so pale?
Will, when looking well can't move her,
    Looking ill prevail?
    Prithee, why so pale?

Why so dull and mute, young sinner?
    Prithee, why so mute?
Will, when speaking well can't win her,
    Saying nothing do't?
    Prithee, why so mute?

Quit, quit for shame! This will not move;
    This cannot take her.
If of herself she will not love,
    Nothing can make her:
    The devil take her!

SIR JOHN SUCKLING

TO ALTHEA, FROM PRISON

WHEN Love with unconfinéd wings
    Hovers within my gates,
And my divine Althea brings
    To whisper at the grates;
When I lie tangled in her hair
    And fettered to her eye,
The gods that wanton in the air
    Know no such liberty.

When flowing cups run swiftly round
   With no allaying Thames,
Our careless heads with roses bound,
   Our hearts with loyal flames;
When thirsty grief in wine we steep,
   When healths and draughts go free,
Fishes that tipple in the deep
   Know no such liberty.

When, like committed linnets, I
   With shriller throat shall sing
The sweetness, mercy, majesty,
   And glories of my King;
When I shall voice aloud how good
   He is, how great should be;
Enlargéd winds that curl the flood
   Know no such liberty.

Stone walls do not a prison make,
   Nor iron bars a cage;
Minds innocent and quiet take
   That for an hermitage;
If I have freedom in my love,
   And in my soul am free;
Angels alone, that soar above,
   Enjoy such liberty.

SIR RICHARD LOVELACE

TO LUCASTA, GOING TO THE WARS

TELL me not, Sweet, I am unkind,
    That from the nunnery
Of thy chaste breast and quiet mind
    To war and arms I fly.

True; a new mistress now I chase,
    The first foe in the field;
And with a stronger faith embrace
    A sword, a horse, a shield.

Yet this inconstancy is such
    As you too shall adore;
I could not love thee, Dear, so much,
    Lov'd I not Honour more.

SIR RICHARD LOVELACE

BERMUDAS

WHERE the remote Bermudas ride
    In the ocean's bosom unespied,
From a small boat, that row'd along,
The list'ning winds receiv'd this song:

'What should we do but sing his praise
That led us through the wat'ry maze,
Unto an isle so long unknown,
And yet far kinder than our own?
Where he the huge Sea-Monsters wracks,
That lift the deep upon their backs.
He lands us on a grassy stage,

Safe from the storms, and prelate's rage.
He gave us this eternal Spring,
Which here enamels everything;
And sends the fowls to us in care,
On daily visits through the air.
He hangs in shades the orange bright,
Like golden lamps in a green night.
And does in the pomegranates close
Jewels more rich than Ormus shows.
He makes the figs our mouths to meet
And throws the melons at our feet.
But apples plants of such a price,
No tree could ever bear them twice.
With cedars, chosen by his hand
From Lebanon, he stores the land.
And makes the hollow seas that roar
Proclaim the ambergris on shore.
He cast (of which we rather[1] boast)
The Gospel's pearl upon our coast.
And in these rocks for us did frame
A temple, where to sound his name.
Oh let our voice his praise exalt
Till it arrive at Heaven's vault:
Which thence, perhaps, rebounding may
Echo beyond the Mexique bay.'

Thus sung they, in the English boat,
A holy and a cheerful note,
And all the way, to guide their chime,
With falling oars they kept the time.

ANDREW MARVELL

[1] more justly, with better reason

A SONG FOR ST. CECILIA'S DAY

FROM harmony, from heavenly harmony
    This universal frame began;
  When nature underneath a heap
      Of jarring atoms lay,
      And could not heave her head,
The tuneful voice was heard from high,
      Arise, ye more than dead.
Then cold and hot and moist and dry
    In order to their stations leap,
      And Music's power obey.
From harmony, from heavenly harmony
      This universal frame began:
      From harmony to harmony
Through all the compass of the notes it ran,
The diapason closing full in Man.

What passion cannot Music raise and quell?
      When Jubal struck the chorded shell,
    His listening brethren stood around,
      And, wondering, on their faces fell
    To worship that celestial sound:
Less than a God they thought there could not dwell
      Within the hollow of that shell,
      That spoke so sweetly, and so well.
What passion cannot Music raise and quell?

The trumpet's loud clangour
    Excites us to arms
With shrill notes of anger
    And mortal alarms.
The double double double beat
    Of the thundering drum
    Cries, Hark the foes come;
Charge, charge, 'tis too late to retreat.

The soft complaining flute
In dying notes discovers
The woes of hopeless lovers,
Whose dirge is whispered by the warbling lute.

Sharp violins proclaim
Their jealous pangs and desperation,
Fury, frantic indignation,
Depth of pains and height of passion,
    For the fair, disdainful dame.

But O, what art can teach,
What human voice can reach
    The sacred organ's praise?
Notes inspiring holy love,
Notes that wing their heavenly ways
    To mend the choirs above.

Orpheus could lead the savage race,
And trees unrooted left their place,
    Sequacious[1] of the lyre;
But bright Cecilia rais'd the wonder higher:

[1] following

When to her organ vocal breath was given,
An angel heard, and straight appear'd
    Mistaking Earth for Heaven.

GRAND CHORUS

As from the power of sacred lays
    The spheres began to move,
And sung the great Creator's praise
    To all the Blest above;
So, when the last and dreadful hour
This crumbling pageant shall devour,
The trumpet shall be heard on high,
The dead shall live, the living die,
And Music shall untune the sky.

JOHN DRYDEN

CHARACTER OF GEORGE VILLIERS, DUKE OF BUCKINGHAM

A MAN so various, that he seemed to be
Not one, but all mankind's epitome.
Stiff in opinions, always in the wrong;
Was everything by starts, and nothing long:
But, in the course of one revolving moon,
Was chemist, fiddler, statesman, and buffoon;
Then all for women, painting, rhyming, drinking,
Besides ten thousand freaks that died in thinking.
Blest madman, who could every hour employ,
With something new to wish, or to enjoy!

Railing and praising were his usual themes;
And both (to show his judgement) in extremes:
So over violent, or over civil,
That every man, with him, was God or Devil.
In squandering wealth was his peculiar art:
Nothing went unrewarded, but desert.
Beggared by fools, whom still he found too late:
He had his jest, and they had his estate.

JOHN DRYDEN

EPITAPH ON CHARLES II

HERE lies a Great and Mighty King,
  Whose Promise none rely'd on,
He never said a Foolish thing
  Nor ever did a Wise one.

JOHN WILMOT, EARL OF ROCHESTER

FROM 'AN ESSAY ON MAN'

KNOW then thyself, presume not God to scan;
  The proper study of mankind is *Man*.
Placed on this isthmus of a middle state,
A being darkly wise, and rudely great:
With too much knowledge for the sceptic side,
With too much weakness for the stoic's pride,
He hangs between; in doubt to act, or rest;
In doubt to deem himself a god, or beast;
In doubt his mind or body to prefer;
Born but to die, and reasoning but to err;
Alike in ignorance, his reason such,
Whether he thinks too little, or too much:

Chaos of thought and passion, all confused;
Still by himself abused, or disabused;
Created half to rise, and half to fall;
Great lord of all things, yet a prey to all;
Sole judge of truth, in endless error hurl'd:
The glory, jest, and riddle of the world!

ALEXANDER POPE

FROM 'AN ESSAY ON CRITICISM'

A LITTLE learning is a dangerous thing;
Drink deep, or taste not the Pierian spring:
There shallow draughts intoxicate the brain,
And drinking largely sobers us again.
Fired at first sight with what the Muse imparts,
In fearless youth we tempt the heights of arts,
While from the bounded level of our mind
Short views we take, nor see the lengths behind;
But more advanced, behold with strange surprise
New distant scenes of endless science rise!
So pleased at first the towering Alps we try,
Mount o'er the vales, and seem to tread the sky,
The eternal snows appear already pass'd,
And the first clouds and mountains seem the last:
But, those attain'd, we tremble to survey
The growing labours of the lengthen'd way,
The increasing prospect tires our wandering eyes,
Hills peep o'er hills, and Alps on Alps arise!

ALEXANDER POPE

ELEGY WRITTEN IN A COUNTRY CHURCHYARD

THE curfew tolls the knell of parting day,
The lowing herd wind slowly o'er the lea,
The plowman homeward plods his weary way,
And leaves the world to darkness and to me.

Now fades the glimmering landscape on the sight,
And all the air a solemn stillness holds,
Save where the beetle wheels his droning flight,
And drowsy tinklings lull the distant folds;

Save that from yonder ivy-mantled tower
The moping owl does to the moon complain
Of such as, wand'ring near her secret bower,
Molest her ancient solitary reign.

Beneath those rugged elms, that yew-tree's shade,
Where heaves the turf in many a mould'ring heap,
Each in his narrow cell for ever laid,
The rude Forefathers of the hamlet sleep.

The breezy call of incense-breathing Morn,
The swallow twitt'ring from the straw-built shed,
The cock's shrill clarion, or the echoing horn,
No more shall rouse them from their lowly bed.

For them no more the blazing hearth shall burn,
Or busy housewife ply her evening care:
No children run to lisp their sire's return,
Or climb his knees the envied kiss to share.

Oft did the harvest to their sickle yield,
Their furrow oft the stubborn glebe has broke;
How jocund did they drive their team afield!
How bow'd the woods beneath their sturdy stroke!

Let not Ambition mock their useful toil,
Their homely joys, and destiny obscure;
Nor Grandeur hear with a disdainful smile
The short and simple annals of the poor.

The boast of heraldry, the pomp of power,
And all that beauty, all that wealth e'er gave,
Await alike th' inevitable hour.
The paths of glory lead but to the grave.

Nor you, ye proud, impute to these the fault,
If Memory o'er their tomb no trophies raise,
Where through the long-drawn aisle and fretted vault
The pealing anthem swells the note of praise.

Can storied urn or animated bust
Back to its mansion call the fleeting breath?
Can Honour's voice provoke the silent dust,
Or Flattery soothe the dull cold ear of Death?

Perhaps in this neglected spot is laid
Some heart once pregnant with celestial fire;
Hands that the rod of empire might have sway'd,
Or waked to ecstasy the living lyre.

But Knowledge to their eyes her ample page
Rich with the spoils of time did ne'er unroll:
Chill Penury repress'd their noble rage,
And froze the genial current of the soul.

Full many a gem of purest ray serene
The dark unfathom'd caves of ocean bear:
Full many a flower is born to blush unseen,
And waste its sweetness on the desert air.

Some village-Hampden, that with dauntless breast
The little tyrant of his fields withstood;
Some mute inglorious Milton here may rest,
Some Cromwell guiltless of his country's blood.

Th' applause of list'ning senates to command,
The threats of pain and ruin to despise,
To scatter plenty o'er a smiling land,
And read their history in a nation's eyes,

Their lot forbad: nor circumscribed alone
Their growing virtues, but their crimes confined;
Forbad to wade through slaughter to a throne,
And shut the gates of mercy on mankind;

The struggling pangs of conscious truth to hide,
To quench the blushes of ingenuous shame,
Or heap the shrine of Luxury and Pride
With incense kindled at the Muse's flame.

Far from the madding crowd's ignoble strife,
Their sober wishes never learn'd to stray;
Along the cool sequester'd vale of life
They kept the noiseless tenour of their way.

Yet ev'n these bones from insult to protect
Some frail memorial still erected nigh,
With uncouth rhymes and shapeless sculpture deck'd,
Implores the passing tribute of a sigh.

Their name, their years, spelt by th' unletter'd muse,
The place of fame and elegy supply:
And many a holy text around she strews,
That teach the rustic moralist to die.

For who, to dumb Forgetfulness a prey,
This pleasing anxious being e'er resign'd,
Left the warm precincts of the cheerful day,
Nor cast one longing lingering look behind?

On some fond breast the parting soul relies,
Some pious drops the closing eye requires;
Ev'n from the tomb the voice of Nature cries,
Ev'n in our ashes live their wonted fires.

For thee, who, mindful of th' unhonour'd Dead,
Dost in these lines their artless tale relate;
If chance, by lonely contemplation led,
Some kindred spirit shall inquire thy fate,

Haply some hoary-headed swain may say,
'Oft have we seen him at the peep of dawn
Brushing with hasty steps the dews away
To meet the sun upon the upland lawn.

'There at the foot of yonder nodding beech
That wreathes its old fantastic roots so high,
His listless length at noontide would he stretch,
And pore upon the brook that babbles by.

'Hard by yon wood, now smiling as in scorn,
Mutt'ring his wayward fancies he would rove,
Now drooping, woeful wan, like one forlorn,
Or crazed with care, or cross'd in hopeless love.

'One morn I miss'd him on the custom'd hill,
Along the heath, and near his favourite tree;
Another came; nor yet beside the rill,
Nor up the lawn, nor at the wood was he;

'The next with dirges due in sad array
Slow through the church-way path we saw him borne.
Approach and read (for thou canst read) the lay
Graved on the stone beneath yon aged thorn.'

The Epitaph

Here rests his head upon the lap of Earth
A Youth to Fortune and to Fame unknown.
Fair Science frown'd not on his humble birth,
And Melancholy mark'd him for her own.

Large was his bounty, and his soul sincere,
Heaven did a recompense as largely send:
He gave to Misery all he had, a tear,
He gain'd from Heaven ('twas all he wish'd) a friend.

No farther seek his merits to disclose,
Or draw his frailties from their dread abode,
(There they alike in trembling hope repose,)
The bosom of his Father and his God.

THOMAS GRAY

HOW SLEEP THE BRAVE

How sleep the brave, who sink to rest,
By all their country's wishes blest!
When Spring, with dewy fingers cold,
Returns to deck their hallow'd mould,
She there shall dress a sweeter sod
Than Fancy's feet have ever trod.

By fairy hands their knell is rung,
By forms unseen their dirge is sung;
There Honour comes, a pilgrim grey,
To bless the turf that wraps their clay,
And Freedom shall awhile repair
To dwell, a weeping hermit, there!

WILLIAM COLLINS

FROM 'THE VILLAGE'

Lo! where the heath, with withering brake grown o'er,
Lends the light turf that warms the neighbouring
   poor;
From thence a length of burning sand appears,
Where the thin harvest waves its wither'd ears;
Rank weeds, that every art and care defy,
Reign o'er the land, and rob the blighted rye:
There thistles stretch their prickly arms afar,
And to the ragged infant threaten war;
There poppies, nodding, mock the hope of toil;
There the blue bugloss paints the sterile soil;
Hardy and high, above the slender sheaf,
The slimy mallow waves her silky leaf;
O'er the young shoot the charlock throws a shade,
And clasping tares cling round the sickly blade;
With mingled tints the rocky coasts abound,
And a sad splendour vainly shines around.

GEORGE CRABBE

THE VILLAGE SCHOOLMASTER
From THE DESERTED VILLAGE

BESIDE yon straggling fence that skirts the way,
With blossomed furze unprofitably gay,
There, in his noisy mansion, skilled to rule,
The village master taught his little school;
A man severe he was, and stern to view,
I knew him well, and every truant knew;
Well had the boding tremblers learned to trace
The day's disasters in his morning face;
Full well they laughed, with counterfeited glee,
At all his jokes, for many a joke had he: —
Full well the busy whisper, circling round,
Conveyed the dismal tidings when he frowned;
Yet he was kind, or, if severe in aught,
The love he bore to learning was in fault;
The village all declared how much he knew;
'Twas certain he could write, and cipher too;
Lands he could measure, terms and tides presage,
And even the story ran that he could gauge;
In arguing, too, the parson owned his skill,
For, even though vanquished, he could argue still;
While words of learnéd length and thundering sound
Amazed the gazing rustics ranged around;
And still they gazed, and still the wonder grew
That one small head could carry all he knew.

OLIVER GOLDSMITH

Being the my Shrine of Art

AH! SUN-FLOWER

Aн, sun-flower! weary of time,
Who countest the steps of the sun;
Seeking after that sweet golden clime,
Where the traveller's journey is done;

Where the youth pined away with desire,
And the pale virgin shrouded in snow,
Arise from their graves, and aspire
Where my sun-flower wishes to go.

WILLIAM BLAKE

FROM THE PREFACE TO 'MILTON'

And did those feet in ancient time
Walk upon England's mountains green?
And was the holy Lamb of God
   On England's pleasant pastures seen?

And did the Countenance Divine
   Shine forth upon our clouded hills?
And was Jerusalem builded here
   Among these dark Satanic Mills?

Bring me my bow of burning gold!
   Bring me my arrows of desire!
Bring me my spear!   O clouds, unfold!
   Bring me my chariot of fire!

I will not cease from mental fight,
  Nor shall my sword sleep in my hand,
Till we have built Jerusalem
  In England's green and pleasant land.

WILLIAM BLAKE

HOW SWEET I ROAM'D FROM FIELD TO FIELD

How sweet I roam'd from field to field
  And tasted all the summer's pride,
Till I the Prince of Love beheld
Who in the sunny beams did glide!

He show'd me lilies for my hair,
And blushing roses for my brow;
He led me through his gardens fair
Where all his golden pleasures grow.

With sweet May dews my wings were wet,
And Phoebus fir'd my vocal rage;
He caught me in his silken net,
And shut me in his golden cage.

He loves to sit and hear me sing,
Then, laughing, sports and plays with me;
Then stretches out my golden wing,
And mocks my loss of liberty.

WILLIAM BLAKE

FROM 'AUGURIES OF INNOCENCE'

To see a world in a grain of sand,
And a heaven in a wild flower,
Hold infinity in the palm of your hand,
And eternity in an hour.

A robin redbreast in a cage
Puts all Heaven in a rage.
A dove-house fill'd with doves and pigeons
Shudders Hell thro' all its regions.
A dog starv'd at his master's gate
Predicts the ruin of the State.
A horse misus'd upon the road
Calls to Heaven for human blood.
Each outcry of the hunted hare
A fibre from the brain does tear.
A skylark wounded in the wing,
A cherubim does cease to sing.
The game-cock clipped and arm'd for fight
Does the rising sun affright.
Every wolf's and lion's howl
Raises from Hell a human soul.
The wild deer, wandering here and there,
Keeps the human soul from care.
The lamb misus'd breeds public strife,
And yet forgives the butcher's knife. . . .
He who shall hurt the little wren
Shall never be belov'd by men.

WILLIAM BLAKE

FROM THE WITCHES' CHANT, FROM 'ALL-HALLOW-EVE'

(The witches are described as piercing a waxen image of their enemy with bodkins in the traditional manner)

SLEEP'ST thou, wakest thou, lord of the wind?
Mount thy steeds and gallop them blind,
Leave the red thunder-bolt lagging behind;
And the long-tail'd fiery dragon outfly,
The rocket of heaven, the bomb of the sky;
Over the dog-star, over the wain,
Over the cloud and the rainbow's mane:
Over the mountain and over the sea,
Haste, haste, haste to me!

(They pierce the Figure alternately.)

Take that for trouble!
And that for smart!
And that for the pang that seeks the heart!
That for madness!
And that for thrall!
And that for conscience, the worst of all!

JAMES HOGG

DAFFODILS

I WANDERED lonely as a cloud
That floats on high o'er vales and hills,
When all at once I saw a crowd,
A host, of golden daffodils;
Beside the lake, beneath the trees,
Fluttering and dancing in the breeze.

Continuous as the stars that shine
And twinkle on the Milky Way,
They stretched in never-ending line
Along the margin of a bay;
Ten thousand saw I at a glance,
Tossing their heads in sprightly dance.

The waves beside them danced; but they
Out-did the sparkling waves in glee:
A poet could not but be gay,
In such a jocund company:
I gazed—and gazed—but little thought
What wealth the show to me had brought:

For oft, when on my couch I lie
In vacant or in pensive mood,
They flash upon that inward eye
Which is the bliss of solitude;
And then my heart with pleasure fills,
And dances with the daffodils.

WILLIAM WORDSWORTH

THE SOLITARY REAPER

BEHOLD her, single in the field,
Yon solitary highland lass!
Reaping and singing by herself;
Stop here, or gently pass!
Alone she cuts and binds the grain,
And sings a melancholy strain;
O listen! for the vale profound
Is overflowing with the sound.

No nightingale did ever chaunt
More welcome notes to weary bands
Of travellers in some shady haunt,
Among Arabian sands:
A voice so thrilling ne'er was heard
In spring-time from the cuckoo-bird,
Breaking the silence of the seas
Among the farthest Hebrides.

Will no one tell me what she sings?—
Perhaps the plaintive numbers flow
For old, unhappy, far-off things,
And battles long ago:
Or is it some more humble lay,
Familiar matter of to-day?
Some natural sorrow, loss, or pain,
That has been, and may be again?

Whate'er the theme, the maiden sang
As if her song could have no ending;
I saw her singing at her work,
And o'er the sickle bending;—
I listened, motionless and still;
And, as I mounted up the hill,
The music in my heart I bore
Long after it was heard no more.

WILLIAM WORDSWORTH

COMPOSED UPON WESTMINSTER BRIDGE

EARTH has not anything to show more fair:
Dull would he be of soul who could pass by
A sight so touching in its majesty:
This City now doth like a garment wear
The beauty of the morning; silent, bare,
Ships, towers, domes, theatres, and temples lie
Open unto the fields, and to the sky;
All bright and glittering in the smokeless air.
Never did sun more beautifully steep
In his first splendour, valley, rock, or hill;
Ne'er saw I, never felt, a calm so deep!
The river glideth at his own sweet will:
Dear God! the very houses seem asleep;
And all that mighty heart is lying still!

WILLIAM WORDSWORTH

SONNET

IT is a beauteous evening, calm and free,
The holy time is quiet as a nun
Breathless with adoration; the broad sun
Is sinking down in its tranquillity;
The gentleness of heaven broods o'er the sea:
Listen! the mighty being is awake,
And doth with his eternal motion make
A sound like thunder—everlastingly.
Dear Child! dear Girl! that walkest with me here,
If thou appear untouched by solemn thought,
Thy nature is not therefore less divine:
Thou liest in Abraham's bosom all the year;
And worshipp'st at the temple's inner shrine,
God being with thee when we know it not.

WILLIAM WORDSWORTH

SONNET

WITH ships the sea was sprinkled far and nigh,
    Like stars in heaven, and joyously it showed;
Some lying fast at anchor in the road,
Some veering up and down, one knew not why.
A goodly vessel did I then espy
Come like a giant from a haven broad;
And lustily along the bay she strode,
Her tackling rich, and of apparel high.
This ship was nought to me, nor I to her,
Yet I pursued her with a lover's look;
This ship to all the rest did I prefer:
When will she turn, and whither? She will brook
No tarrying; where she comes the winds must stir:
On went she, and due north her journey took.

WILLIAM WORDSWORTH

THE RAINBOW

MY heart leaps up when I behold
  A rainbow in the sky:
So was it when my life began;
So is it now I am a man;
So be it when I shall grow old,
  Or let me die!
The child is father of the man;
And I could wish my days to be
Bound each to each by natural piety.

WILLIAM WORDSWORTH

FROM 'THE LAY OF THE LAST MINSTREL'

BREATHES there the man, with soul so dead,
  Who never to himself hath said,
  'This is my own, my native land!'
Whose heart hath ne'er within him burn'd,
As home his footsteps he hath turn'd
  From wandering on a foreign strand!
If such there breathe, go, mark him well;
For him no Minstrel raptures swell;
High though his titles, proud his name,
Boundless his wealth as wish can claim;
Despite those titles, power, and pelf,
The wretch, concentred all in self,
Living, shall forfeit fair renown,
And, doubly dying, shall go down
To the vile dust, from whence he sprung,
Unwept, unhonour'd, and unsung.

WALTER SCOTT

THE RIME OF THE ANCIENT MARINER

Argument

How a ship having passed the Line was driven by storms to the cold Country towards the South Pole; and how from thence she made her course to the tropical Latitude of the Great Pacific Ocean; and of the strange things that befel; and in what manner the Ancient Mariner came back to his own Country.

PART I

I{T} is an ancient Mariner,
And he stoppeth one of three.
'By thy long grey beard and glittering eye,
Now wherefore stopp'st thou me?

An ancient Mariner meeteth three Gallants bidden to a wedding-feast, and detaineth one.

The Bridegroom's doors are open'd wide,
And I am next of kin;
The guests are met, the feast is set:
May'st hear the merry din.'

He holds him with his skinny hand,
'There was a ship,' quoth he.
'Hold off! unhand me, grey-beard loon!'
Eftsoons his hand dropt he.

He holds him with his glittering eye—
The Wedding-Guest stood still,
And listens like a three years' child:
The Mariner hath his will.

The Wedding-Guest is spellbound by the eye of the old seafaring man, and constrained to hear his tale.

The Wedding-Guest sat on a stone:
He cannot choose but hear;
And thus spake on that ancient man,
The bright-eyed Mariner.

'The ship was cheered, the harbour cleared,
Merrily did we drop
Below the kirk, below the hill,
Below the lighthouse top.

The Mariner
tells how the
ship sailed
southward with
a good wind
and fair
weather, till
it reached the
line.

The Sun came up upon the left,
Out of the sea came he!
And he shone bright, and on the right
Went down into the sea.

Higher and higher every day,
Till over the mast at noon—'
The Wedding-Guest here beat his breast,
For he heard the loud bassoon.

The Wedding-
Guest heareth
the bridal
music; but the
Mariner con-
tinueth his tale.

The bride hath paced into the hall,
Red as a rose is she;
Nodding their heads before her goes
The merry minstrelsy.

The Wedding-Guest he beat his breast,
Yet he cannot choose but hear;
And thus spake on that ancient man,
The bright-eyed Mariner.

'And now the Storm-blast came, and he
Was tyrannous and strong:
He struck with his o'ertaking wings,
And chased us south along.

With sloping masts and dipping prow,
As who pursued with yell and blow
Still treads the shadow of his foe,
And forward bends his head,
The ship drove fast, loud roared the blast,
And southward aye we fled.

And now there came both mist and snow,
And it grew wondrous cold:
And ice, mast-high, came floating by,
As green as emerald.

And through the drifts the snowy clifts
Did send a dismal sheen:
Nor shapes of men nor beasts we ken—
The ice was all between.

The ice was here, the ice was there,
The ice was all around:
It crack'd and growled, and roared and
    howled,
Like noises in a swound!

At length did cross an Albatross,
Thorough the fog it came;
As if it had been a Christian soul,
We hailed it in God's name.

The ship driven by a storm toward the south pole.

The land of ice, and of fearful sounds, where no living thing was to be seen.

Till a great sea-bird, called the Albatross, came through the snow-fog, and was received with great joy and hospitality.

— 235 —

It ate the food it ne'er had eat,
And round and round it flew.
The ice did split with a thunder-fit;
The helmsman steer'd us through!

And lo! the Albatross proveth a bird of good omen, and followeth the ship as it returned northward through fog and floating ice.

And a good south wind sprung up behind
The Albatross did follow,
And every day, for food or play,
Came to the mariners' hollo!

In mist or cloud, on mast or shroud,
It perched for vespers nine;
Whiles all the night, through fog-smoke
    white,
Glimmer'd the white Moonshine.'

The ancient Mariner inhospitably killeth the pious bird of good omen.

'God save thee, ancient Mariner!
From the fiends, that plague thee thus!—
Why look'st thou so?'—'With my crossbow
I shot the Albatross.

PART II

The Sun now rose upon the right:
Out of the sea came he,
Still hid in mist, and on the left,
Went down into the sea.

And the good south wind still blew behind,
But no sweet bird did follow,
Nor any day for food or play
Came to the mariners' hollo!

And I had done a hellish thing,
And it would work 'em woe:
For all averred, I had kill'd the bird
That made the breeze to blow.
Ah wretch! said they, the bird to slay,
That made the breeze to blow!

His shipmates cry out against the ancient Mariner, for killing the bird of good luck.

Nor dim nor red, like God's own head,
The glorious Sun uprist:
Then all averred I had kill'd the bird
That brought the fog and mist.
'Twas right, said they, such birds to slay,
That bring the fog and mist.

But when the fog cleared off, they justify the same, and thus make themselves accomplices in the crime.

The fair breeze blew, the white foam flew,
The furrow followed free;
We were the first that ever burst
Into that silent sea.

The fair breeze continues; the ship enters the Pacific Ocean, and sails northward, even till it reaches the Line.

Down dropt the breeze, the sails dropt down,
'Twas sad as sad could be;
And we did speak only to break
The silence of the sea!

The ship hath been suddenly becalmed.

All in a hot and copper sky,
The bloody Sun, at noon,
Right up above the mast did stand,
No bigger than the Moon.

Day after day, day after day,
We stuck, nor breath nor motion;
As idle as a painted ship
Upon a painted ocean.

And the Alba-
tross begins to
be avenged.

Water, water, everywhere,
And all the boards did shrink;
Water, water, everywhere,
Nor any drop to drink.

The very deep did rot: O Christ!
That ever this should be!
Yea, slimy things did crawl with legs
Upon the slimy sea.

About, about, in reel and rout
The death-fires danced at night;
The water, like a witch's oils,
Burnt green, and blue and white.

A Spirit had
followed them;
one of the in-
visible inhabi-
tants of this
planet, neither
departed souls
nor angels; con-
cerning whom
the learned Jew, Josephus, and the Platonic Constantinopolitan, Michael Psellus, may be
consulted. They are very numerous, and there is no climate or element without one or
more.

And some in dreams assuréd were
Of the Spirit that plagued us so;
Nine fathom deep he had follow'd us
From the land of mist and snow.

And every tongue, through utter drought,
Was withered at the root;
We could not speak, no more than if
We had been choked with soot.

The shipmates
in their sore
distress, would
fain throw the
whole guilt on
the ancient
Mariner: in
sign whereof
they hang the
dead sea-bird
round his neck.

Ah! well a-day! what evil looks
Had I from old and young!
Instead of the cross, the Albatross
About my neck was hung.

PART III

There passed a weary time. Each throat
Was parched, and glazed each eye.
A weary time! a weary time!
How glazed each weary eye,
When looking westward, I beheld
A something in the sky.

The ancient
Mariner be-
holdeth a sign
in the element
far off.

At first it seemed a little speck,
And then it seemed a mist;
It moved and moved, and took at last
A certain shape, I wist.

A speck, a mist, a shape, I wist!
And still it neared and neared:
As if it dodged a water-sprite,
It plunged, and tacked, and veered.

With throats unslaked, with black lips baked,
We could nor laugh nor wail;
Through utter drought all dumb we stood!
I bit my arm, I sucked the blood,
And cried, A sail! a sail!

At its nearer
approach, it
seemeth him
to be a ship;
and at a dear
ransom he
freeth his
speech from
the bonds of
thirst.

With throats unslaked, with black lips baked,
Agape they heard me call:
Gramercy! they for joy did grin,
And all at once their breath drew in,
As they were drinking all.

A flash of joy;

And horror follows. For can it be a ship that comes onward without wind or tide?

See! see! (I cried) she tacks no more!
Hither to work us weal;
Without a breeze, without a tide,
She steadies with upright keel!

The western wave was all aflame,
The day was well nigh done!
Almost upon the western wave
Rested the broad, bright Sun;
When that strange shape drove suddenly
Betwixt us and the Sun.

It seemeth him but the skeleton of a ship.

And straight the Sun was flecked with bars
(Heaven's Mother send us grace!)
As if through a dungeon-grate he peer'd
With broad and burning face.

Alas! (thought I, and my heart beat loud)
How fast she nears and nears!
Are those *her* sails that glance in the Sun,
Like restless gossameres?

And its ribs are seen as bars on the face of the setting Sun. The Spectre-Woman and her Death-mate, and no other, on board the skeleton ship.

Are those *her* ribs through which the Sun
Did peer, as through a grate?
And is that Woman all her crew?
Is that a Death? and are there two?
Is Death that Woman's mate?

Like vessel, like crew!

Her lips were red, *her* looks were free,
Her locks were yellow as gold:

– 240 –

Her skin was as white as leprosy,
The Nightmare Life-in-Death was she,
Who thicks man's blood with cold.

The naked hulk alongside came,
And the twain were casting dice;
"The game is done! I've won! I've won!"
Quoth she, and whistles thrice.

Death and
Life-in-Death
have diced for
the ship's crew,
and she (the
latter) winneth
the ancient
Mariner.

The Sun's rim dips; the stars rush out:
At one stride comes the dark;
With far-heard whisper, o'er the sea,
Off shot the spectre-bark.

No twilight
within the
courts of the
Sun.

We listened and looked sideways up!
Fear at my heart, as at a cup,
My life-blood seemed to sip!
The stars were dim, and thick the night,
The steersman's face by his lamp gleamed
    white;
From the sails the dew did drip—
Till clomb above the eastern bar
The hornéd Moon, with one bright star
Within the nether tip.

At the rising
of the Moon,

One after one, by the star-dogged Moon,
Too quick for groan or sigh,
Each turn'd his face with a ghastly pang,
And cursed me with his eye.

One after
another,

– 241 –

His shipmates drop down dead.

Four times fifty living men
(And I heard nor sigh nor groan)
With heavy thump, a lifeless lump,
They dropp'd down one by one.

But Life-in-Death begins her work on the ancient Mariner.

The souls did from their bodies fly,—
They fled to bliss or woe!
And every soul, it passed me by
Like the whizz of my crossbow!'

PART IV

The Wedding-Guest feareth that a spirit is talking to him.

'I fear thee, ancient Mariner!
I fear thy skinny hand!
And thou art long, and lank, and brown,
As is the ribbed sea-sand.

I fear thee and thy glittering eye,
And thy skinny hand so brown.'—

But the ancient Mariner assureth him of his bodily life, and proceedeth to relate his horrible penance.

'Fear not, fear not, thou Wedding-Guest!
This body dropt not down.

Alone, alone, all, all alone,
Alone on a wide, wide sea!
And never a saint took pity on
My soul in agony.

He despiseth the creatures of the calm.

The many men, so beautiful!
And they all dead did lie:
And a thousand thousand slimy things
Lived on; and so did I.

– 242 –

I looked upon the rotting sea,
And drew my eyes away;
I look'd upon the rotting deck,
And there the dead men lay.

And envieth
that *they*
should live,
and so many
lie dead.

I looked to heaven, and tried to pray;
But or ever a prayer had gusht,
A wicked whisper came, and made
My heart as dry as dust.

I closed my lids, and kept them close,
And the balls like pulses beat;
But the sky and the sea, and the sea and the
    sky
Lay like a load on my weary eye,
And the dead were at my feet.

The cold sweat melted from their limbs,
Nor rot nor reek did they:
The look with which they looked on me
Had never passed away.

But the curse
liveth for him
in the eye of the
dead men.

An orphan's curse would drag to hell
A spirit from on high;
But oh! more horrible than that
Is the curse in a dead man's eye!
Seven days, seven nights, I saw that curse,
And yet I could not die.

The moving Moon went up the sky,
And nowhere did abide:
Softly she was going up,
And a star or two beside—

In his loneliness and fixedness he yearneth towards the journeying Moon, and the stars that still sojourn, yet still move onward; and every where the blue sky belongs to them, and is their appointed rest and their native country and their own natural homes, which they enter unannounced, as lords that are certainly expected and yet there is a silent joy at their arrival.

Her beams bemocked the sultry main,
Like April hoar-frost spread;
But where the ship's huge shadow lay,
The charméd water burnt alway
A still and awful red.

By the light of the Moon he beholdeth God's creatures of the great calm.

Beyond the shadow of the ship,
I watched the water-snakes:
They moved in tracks of shining white,
And when they reared, the elfish light
Fell off in hoary flakes.

Within the shadow of the ship
I watched their rich attire:
Blue, glossy green, and velvet black,
They coiled and swam; and every track
Was a flash of golden fire.

Their beauty and their happiness.

O happy living things! no tongue
Their beauty might declare:
A spring of love gushed from my heart,

He blesseth them in his heart.

And I blessed them unaware:
Sure my kind saint took pity on me,
And I blessed them unaware.

The self-same moment I could pray;
And from my neck so free
The Albatross fell off, and sank
Like lead into the sea.

The spell begins to break.

PART V

O sleep! it is a gentle thing,
Beloved from pole to pole!
To Mary Queen the praise be given!
She sent the gentle sleep from Heaven,
That slid into my soul.

The silly buckets on the deck,
That had so long remained,
I dreamt that they were filled with dew;
And when I awoke, it rained.

By grace of the holy Mother, the ancient Mariner is refreshed with rain.

My lips were wet, my throat was cold,
My garments all were dank;
Sure I had drunken in my dreams,
And still my body drank.

I moved, and could not feel my limbs:
I was so light—almost
I thought that I had died in sleep,
And was a blessèd ghost.

And soon I heard a roaring wind:
It did not come anear;
But with its sound it shook the sails,
That were so thin and sere.

He heareth sounds and seeth strange sights and commotions in the sky and the element.

The upper air burst into life!
And a hundred fire-flags sheen,
To and fro they were hurried about!
And to and fro, and in and out,
The wan stars danced between.

And the coming wind did roar more loud,
And the sails did sigh like sedge;
And the rain poured down from one black
    cloud;
The Moon was at its edge.

The thick black cloud was cleft, and still
The Moon was at its side:
Like waters shot from some high crag,
The lightning fell with never a jag,
A river steep and wide.

The bodies of
the ship's crew
are inspired,
and the ship
moves on;

The loud wind never reached the ship,
Yet now the ship moved on!
Beneath the lightning and the Moon
The dead men gave a groan.

They groaned, they stirred, they all uprose,
Nor spake, nor moved their eyes;
It had been strange, even in a dream,
To have seen those dead men rise.

– 246 –

The helmsman steered, the ship moved on;
Yet never a breeze up-blew;
The mariners all 'gan work the ropes,
Where they were wont to do;
They raised their limbs like lifeless tools—
We were a ghastly crew.

The body of my brother's son
Stood by me, knee to knee:
The body and I pulled at one rope,
But he said naught to me.'

'I fear thee, ancient Mariner!'
'Be calm, thou Wedding-Guest!
'Twas not those souls that fled in pain,
Which to their corses came again,
But a troop of spirits blest:

But not by
the souls of
the men, nor
by daemons of
earth or middle
air, but by a
blessed troop
of angelic
spirits, sent
down by the
invocation of
the guardian
saint.

For when it dawned—they dropped their
    arms,
And clustered round the mast;
Sweet sounds rose slowly through their
    mouths,
And from their bodies passed.

Around, around, flew each sweet sound,
Then darted to the Sun;
Slowly the sounds came back again,
Now mixed, now one by one.

Sometimes a-dropping from the sky
I heard the skylark sing;
Sometimes all little birds that are,
How they seemed to fill the sea and air
With their sweet jargoning!

And now 'twas like all instruments,
Now like a lonely flute;
And now it is an angel's song,
That makes the heavens be mute.

It ceased; yet still the sails made on
A pleasant noise till noon,
A noise like of a hidden brook
In the leafy month of June,
That to the sleeping woods all night
Singeth a quiet tune.

Till noon we quietly sailed on,
Yet never a breeze did breathe:
Slowly and smoothly went the ship,
Moved onward from beneath.

The lonesome Spirit from the south-pole carries on the ship as far as the Line, in obedience to the angelic troop, but still requireth vengeance.

Under the keel nine fathom deep,
From the land of mist and snow,
The Spirit slid: and it was he
That made the ship to go.
The sails at noon left off their tune,
And the ship stood still also.

The Sun, right up above the mast,
Had fixed her to the ocean:
But in a minute she 'gan stir,
With a short uneasy motion—
Backwards and forwards half her length
With a short uneasy motion.

Then like a pawing horse let go,
She made a sudden bound:
It flung the blood into my head,
And I fell down in a swound.

How long in that same fit I lay,
I have not to declare;
But ere my living life returned,
I heard, and in my soul discerned
Two voices in the air.

"Is it he?" quoth one, "is this the man?
By him who died on cross,
With his cruel bow he laid full low
The harmless Albatross.

The Spirit who bideth by himself
In the land of mist and snow,
He loved the bird that loved the man
Who shot him with his bow."

The other was a softer voice,
As soft as honey-dew:
Quoth he, "The man hath penance done,
And penance more will do."

The Polar
Spirit's fellow-
daemons, the
invisible inhabi-
tants of the
element, take
part in his
wrong; and
two of them
relate, one to
the other, that
penance long
and heavy for
the ancient
Mariner hath
been accorded
to the Polar
Spirit, who
returneth
southward.

PART VI

First Voice:

"But tell me, tell me! speak again,
Thy soft response renewing—
What makes that ship drive on so fast?
What is the ocean doing?"

Second Voice:

"Still as a slave before his lord,
The ocean hath no blast;
His great bright eye most silently
Up to the Moon is cast—

If he may know which way to go;
For she guides him smooth or grim.
See, brother, see! how graciously
She looketh down on him."

First Voice:

The Mariner
hath been cast
into a trance;
for the angelic
power causeth
the vessel to
drive northward
faster than
human life
could endure.

"But why drives on that ship so fast,
Without or wave or wind?"

Second Voice:

"The air is cut away before,
And closes from behind.

Fly, brother, fly! more high, more high!
Or we shall be belated:
For slow and slow that ship will go,
When the Mariner's trance is abated."

I woke, and we were sailing on
As in a gentle weather:
'Twas night, calm night, the moon was high;
The dead men stood together.

The super-
natural motion
is retarded;
the Mariner
awakes, and
his penance
begins anew.

All stood together on the deck,
For a charnel-dungeon fitter:
All fixed on me their stony eyes,
That in the Moon did glitter.

The pang, the curse, with which they died,
Had never pass'd away:
I could not draw my eyes from theirs,
Nor turn them up to pray.

And now this spell was snapt: once more
I viewed the ocean green,
And looked far forth, yet little saw
Of what had else been seen—

The curse is
finally expiated.

Like one that on a lonesome road
Doth walk in fear and dread,
And having once turned round walks on,
And turns no more his head;
Because he knows a frightful fiend
Doth close behind him tread.

But soon there breathed a wind on me,
Nor sound nor motion made:
Its path was not upon the sea,
In ripple or in shade.

It raised my hair, it fanned my cheek
Like a meadow-gale of spring—
It mingled strangely with my fears,
Yet it felt like a welcoming.

Swiftly, swiftly flew the ship,
Yet she sailed softly too:
Sweetly, sweetly blew the breeze—
On me alone it blew.

And the ancient Mariner beholdeth his native country.

Oh! dream of joy! is this indeed
The light-house top I see?
Is this the hill? is this the kirk?
Is this mine own countree?

We drifted o'er the harbour-bar,
And I with sobs did pray—
O let me be awake, my God!
Or let me sleep alway.

The harbour-bay was clear as glass,
So smoothly it was strewn!
And on the bay the moonlight lay,
And the shadow of the Moon.

The rock shone bright, the kirk no less,
That stands above the rock:
The moonlight steep'd in silence
The steady weathercock.

And the bay was white with silent light,
Till rising from the same,
Full many shapes, that shadows were,
In crimson colours came.

The angelic
spirits leave the
dead bodies,

A little distance from the prow
Those crimson shadows were:
I turn'd my eyes upon the deck—
Oh, Christ! what saw I there!

And appear in
their own forms
of light.

Each corse lay flat, lifeless and flat,
And, by the holy rood!
A man all light, a seraph-man,
On every corse there stood.

This seraph-band, each waved his hand:
It was a heavenly sight!
They stood as signals to the land,
Each one a lovely light;

This seraph-band, each waved his hand,
No voice did they impart—
No voice; but oh! the silence sank
Like music on my heart.

But soon I heard the dash of oars,
I heard the Pilot's cheer;
My head was turned perforce away,
And I saw a boat appear.

The Pilot and the Pilot's boy,
I heard them coming fast:
Dear Lord in Heaven! it was a joy
The dead men could not blast.

I saw a third—I heard his voice:
It is the Hermit good!
He singeth loud his godly hymns
That he makes in the wood.
He'll shrieve my soul, he'll wash away
The Albatross's blood.

PART VII

The Hermit of the Wood.

This hermit good lives in that wood
Which slopes down to the sea.
How loudly his sweet voice he rears!
He loves to talk with marineres
That come from a far countree.

He kneels at morn, and noon, and eve—
He hath a cushion plump:
It is the moss that wholly hides
The rotted old oak-stump.

The skiff-boat neared: I heard them talk,
"Why, this is strange, I trow!
Where are those lights so many and fair,
That signal made but now?"

"Strange, by my faith!" the Hermit said— Approacheth
"And they answer'd not our cheer! the ship with
wonder.
The planks look warp'd! and see those sails,
How thin they are and sere!
I never saw aught like to them,
Unless perchance it were

Brown skeletons of leaves that lag
My forest-brook along;
When the ivy-tod is heavy with snow,
And the owlet whoops to the wolf below,
That eats the she-wolf's young."

"Dear Lord! it hath a fiendish look—
(The Pilot made reply)
I am a-fear'd."—"Push on, push on!"
Said the Hermit cheerily

The boat came closer to the ship,
But I nor spake nor stirr'd;
The boat came close beneath the ship,
And straight a sound was heard.

Under the water it rumbled on, The ship sud-
Still louder and more dread: denly sinketh.
It reached the ship, it split the bay;
The ship went down like lead.

The ancient
Mariner is
saved in the
Pilot's boat.

Stunned by that loud and dreadful sound,
Which sky and ocean smote,
Like one that hath been seven days drowned
My body lay afloat;
But swift as dreams, myself I found
Within the Pilot's boat.

Upon the whirl, where sank the ship,
The boat spun round and round;
And all was still, save that the hill
Was telling of the sound.

I moved my lips—the Pilot shrieked
And fell down in a fit;
The holy Hermit raised his eyes,
And prayed where he did sit.

I took the oars: the Pilot's boy,
Who now doth crazy go,
Laughed loud and long, and all the while
His eyes went to and fro.
"Ha! ha!" quoth he, "full plain I see
The Devil knows how to row."

And now, all in my own countree,
I stood on the firm land!
The Hermit stepped forth from the boat,
And scarcely he could stand.

"O shrieve me, shrieve me, holy man!"
The Hermit crossed his brow.
"Say quick," quoth he, "I bid thee say—
What manner of man art thou?"

Forthwith this frame of mine was wrenched
With a woful agony,
Which forced me to begin my tale;
And then it left me free.

Since then, at an uncertain hour,
That agony returns:
And till my ghastly tale is told,
This heart within me burns.

I pass, like night, from land to land;
I have strange power of speech;
That moment that his face I see,
I know the man that must hear me:
To him my tale I teach.

What loud uproar bursts from that door!
The wedding-guests are there:
But in the garden-bower the bride
And bride-maids singing are:
And hark, the little vesper bell,
Which biddeth me to prayer!

O Wedding-Guest! this soul hath been
Alone on a wide, wide sea:
So lonely 'twas, that God Himself
Scarce seeméd there to be.

The ancient Mariner earnestly entreateth the Hermit to shrieve him; and the penance of life falls on him.

And ever and anon throughout his future life an agony constraineth him to travel from land to land;

O sweeter than the marriage-feast,
'Tis sweeter far to me,
To walk together to the kirk
With a goodly company!—

To walk together to the kirk,
And all together pray,
While each to his great Father bends,
Old men, and babes, and loving friends
And youths and maidens gay!

And to teach,
by his own
example,
love and
reverence to
all things
that God
made and
loveth.

Farewell, farewell! but this I tell
To thee, thou Wedding-Guest!
He prayeth well, who loveth well
Both man and bird and beast.

He prayeth best, who loveth best
All things both great and small;
For the dear God who loveth us,
He made and loveth all.'

The Mariner, whose eye is bright,
Whose beard with age is hoar,
Is gone: and now the Wedding-Guest
Turn'd from the bridegroom's door.

He went like one that hath been stunned,
And is of sense forlorn:
A sadder and a wiser man
He rose the morrow morn.

SAMUEL TAYLOR COLERIDGE

ROSE AYLMER

Aн, what avails the sceptred race!
  Ah, what the form divine!
What every virtue, every grace!
  Rose Aylmer, all were thine.

Rose Aylmer, whom these wakeful eyes
  May weep, but never see,
A night of memories and sighs
  I consecrate to thee.

WALTER SAVAGE LANDOR

FINIS

I strove with none, for none was worth my strife,
  Nature I loved and, next to Nature, Art:
I warm'd both hands before the fire of life:
  It sinks, and I am ready to depart.

WALTER SAVAGE LANDOR

OFT IN THE STILLY NIGHT

OFT in the stilly night,
 Ere Slumber's chain has bound me,
Fond Memory brings the light
 Of other days around me;
  The smiles, the tears,
  Of boyhood's years,
  The words of love then spoken;
  The eyes that shone,
  Now dimmed and gone,
  The cheerful hearts now broken!
Thus, in the stilly night,
 Ere Slumber's chain has bound me,
Sad Memory brings the light
 Of other days around me.

When I remember all
 The friends, so linked together,
I've seen around me fall,
 Like leaves in wintry weather;
  I feel like one
  Who treads alone
  Some banquet-hall deserted,
  Whose lights are fled,
  Whose garlands dead,
  And all but he departed!
Thus in the stilly night,
 Ere Slumber's chain has bound me,
Sad Memory brings the light
 Of other days around me.

THOMAS MOORE

NAPOLEON'S FAREWELL

FAREWELL to the Land where the gloom of my glory
Arose and o'ershadowed the earth with her name—
She abandons me now—but the page of her story,
The brightest or blackest, is fill'd with my fame.
I have warred with a world which vanquished me only
When the meteor of Conquest allured me too far;
I have coped with the nations which dread me thus
    lonely,
The last single Captive to millions in war.

Farewell to thee, France! when thy diadem crowned me,
I made thee the gem and the wonder of earth,
But thy weakness decrees I should leave as I found thee,
Decayed in thy glory, and sunk in thy worth.
Oh! for the veteran hearts that were wasted
In strife with the storm, when their battles were won—
Then the Eagle, whose gaze in that moment was blasted,
Had still soared with eyes fixed on victory's sun!

Farewell to thee, France!—but when Liberty rallies
Once more in thy regions, remember me then,—
The violet still grows in the depth of thy valleys;
Though withered, thy tears will unfold it again—
Yet, yet, I may baffle the hosts that surround us,
And yet may thy heart leap awake to my voice—
There are links which must break in the chain that has
    bound us,
Then turn thee and call on the Chief of thy choice!

LORD BYRON

THE OCEAN
(*From* CHILDE HAROLD)

ROLL on, thou deep and dark blue Ocean—roll!
Ten thousand fleets sweep over thee in vain;
Man marks the earth with ruin—his control
Stops with the shore; upon the watery plain
The wrecks are all thy deed, nor doth remain
A shadow of man's ravage, save his own,
When, for a moment, like a drop of rain,
He sinks into thy depths with bubbling groan,
Without a grave, unknell'd, uncoffin'd, and unknown.

His steps are not upon thy paths,—thy fields
Are not a spoil for him,—thou dost arise
And shake him from thee; the vile strength he wields
For earth's destruction thou dost all despise,
Spurning him from thy bosom to the skies,
And send'st him, shivering in thy playful spray
And howling, to his Gods, where haply lies
His petty hope in some near port or bay,
And dashest him again to earth:—there let him lay.

The armaments which thunderstrike the walls
Of rock-built cities, bidding nations quake,
And monarchs tremble in their capitals,
The oak leviathans, whose huge ribs make
Their clay creator the vain title take
Of lord of thee, and arbiter of war—
These are thy toys, and, as the snowy flake,
They melt into thy yeast of waves, which mar
Alike the Armada's pride or spoils of Trafalgár.

Thy shores are empires, changed in all save thee—
Assyria, Greece, Rome, Carthage, what are they?
Thy waters wash'd them power while they were free,
And many a tyrant since; their shores obey
The stranger, slave, or savage; their decay
Has dried up realms to deserts:—not so thou;—
Unchangeable, save to thy wild waves' play,
Time writes no wrinkle on thine azure brow:
Such as creation's dawn beheld, thou rollest now.

Thou glorious mirror, where the Almighty's form
Glasses itself in tempests; in all time,—
Calm or convulsed, in breeze, or gale, or storm,
Icing the pole, or in the torrid clime
Dark-heaving—boundless, endless, and sublime,
The image of eternity, the throne
Of the Invisible; even from out thy slime
The monsters of the deep are made; each zone
Obeys thee; thou goest forth, dread, fathomless, alone.

And I have loved thee, Ocean! and my joy
Of youthful sports was on thy breast to be
Borne, like thy bubbles, onward: from a boy
I wanton'd with thy breakers—they to me
Were a delight; and if the freshening sea
Made them a terror—'t was a pleasing fear,
For I was as it were a child of thee,
And trusted to thy billows far and near,
And laid my hand upon thy mane—as I do here.

LORD BYRON

THE EVE OF WATERLOO
(From CHILDE HAROLD)

THERE was a sound of revelry by night,
  And Belgium's capital had gathered then
Her Beauty and her Chivalry, and bright
The lamps shone o'er fair women and brave men,
A thousand hearts beat happily; and when
Music arose with its voluptuous swell,
Soft eyes looked love to eyes which spake again,
And all went merry as a marriage bell;
But hush! hark! a deep sound strikes like a rising knell!

Did ye not hear it?—No; 'twas but the wind,
Or the car rattling o'er the stony street;
On with the dance! let joy be unconfined;
No sleep till morn, when Youth and Pleasure meet
To chase the glowing hours with flying feet—
But hark!—that heavy sound breaks in once more,
As if the clouds its echo would repeat;
And nearer, clearer, deadlier than before!
Arm! Arm! it is—it is—the cannon's opening roar!

Within a window'd niche of that high hall
Sate Brunswick's fated chieftain; he did hear
That sound the first amidst the festival,
And caught its tone with Death's prophetic ear;
And when they smiled because he deemed it near,
His heart more truly knew that peal too well
Which stretched his father on a bloody bier,
And roused the vengeance blood alone could quell;
He rushed into the field, and, foremost fighting, fell.

Ah! then and there was hurrying to and fro,
And gathering tears, and tremblings of distress,
And cheeks all pale, which but an hour ago
Blushed at the praise of their own loveliness;
And there were sudden partings, such as press
The life from out young hearts, and choking sighs
Which ne'er might be repeated; who could guess
If ever more should meet those mutual eyes,
Since upon night so sweet such awful morn could rise!

And there was mounting in hot haste: the steed,
The mustering squadron, and the clattering car,
Went pouring forward with impetuous speed,
And swiftly forming in the ranks of war;
And the deep thunder peal on peal afar;
And near, the beat of the alarming drum
Roused up the soldier ere the morning star;
While thronged the citizens with terror dumb,
Or whispering, with white lips—'The foe! they come!
    they come!'

And wild and high the 'Cameron's gathering' rose!
The war-note of Lochiel, which Albyn's hills
Have heard, and heard, too, have her Saxon foes:—
How in the noon of night that pibroch thrills,
Savage and shrill! But with the breath which fills
Their mountain-pipe, so fill the mountaineers
With the fierce native daring which instils
The stirring memory of a thousand years,
And Evan's, Donald's fame rings in each clansman's ears!

And Ardennes waves above them her green leaves,
Dewy with nature's tear-drops as they pass,
Grieving, if aught inanimate e'er grieves,
Over the unreturning brave,—alas!
Ere evening to be trodden like the grass
Which now beneath them, but above shall grow
In its next verdure, when this fiery mass
Of living valour, rolling on the foe,
And burning with high hope shall moulder cold and low.

Last noon beheld them full of lusty life,
Last eve in Beauty's circle proudly gay,
The midnight brought the signal-sound of strife,
The morn the marshalling in arms,—the day
Battle's magnificently stern array!
The thunder-clouds close o'er it, which when rent
The earth is covered thick with other clay,
Which her own clay shall cover, heaped and pent,
Rider and horse,—friend, foe,—in one red burial blent!

LORD BYRON

THE ISLES OF GREECE

THE isles of Greece, the isles of Greece!
 Where burning Sappho loved and sung,
Where grew the arts of war and peace,
 Where Delos rose, and Phoebus sprung!
Eternal summer gilds them yet,
But all, except their sun, is set.

The Scian and the Teian muse,
  The hero's harp, the lover's lute,
Have found the fame your shores refuse:
  Their place of birth alone is mute
To sounds which echo further west
Than your sires' 'Islands of the Blest'

The mountains look on Marathon—
  And Marathon looks on the sea;
And musing there an hour alone,
  I dream'd that Greece might still be free;
For, standing on the Persians' grave
I could not deem myself a slave.

A king sate on the rocky brow
  Which looks o'er sea-born Salamis;
And ships, by thousands, lay below,
  And men in nations;—all were his!
He counted them at break of day—
And when the sun set where were they?

And where are they? and where art thou,
  My country? On thy voiceless shore
The heroic lay is tuneless now—
  The heroic bosom beats no more!
And must thy lyre, so long divine,
Degenerate into hands like mine?

'Tis something, in the dearth of fame,
  Though link'd among a fetter'd race,
To feel at least a patriot's shame,
  Even as I sing, suffuse my face;
For what is left the poet here?
For Greeks a blush—for Greece a tear.

Must *we* but weep o'er days more blest?
  Must *we* but blush?—Our fathers bled.
Earth! render back from out thy breast
  A remnant of our Spartan dead!
Of the Three Hundred grant but three,
To make a new Thermopylae!

What, silent still? and silent all?
  Ah! no;—the voices of the dead
Sound like a distant torrent's fall,
  And answer, 'Let one living head,
But one arise,—we come, we come!'
'Tis but the living who are dumb.

In vain—in vain: strike other chords;
  Fill high the cup with Samian wine!
Leave battles to the Turkish hordes,
  And shed the blood of Scio's vine!
Hark! rising to the ignoble call—
How answers each bold Bacchanal!

You have the Pyrrhic dance as yet;
   Where is the Pyrrhic phalanx gone?
Of two such lessons, why forget
   The nobler and the manlier one?
You have the letters Cadmus gave—
Think ye he meant them for a slave?

Fill high the bowl with Samian wine!
   We will not think of themes like these!
It made Anacreon's song divine:
   He served—but served Polycrates—
A tyrant; but our masters then
Were still, at least, our countrymen.

The tyrant of the Chersonese
   Was freedom's best and bravest friend;
That tyrant was Miltiades!
   Oh! that the present hour would lend
Another despot of the kind!
Such chains as his were sure to bind.

Fill high the bowl with Samian wine!
   On Suli's rock, and Parga's shore,
Exists the remnant of a line
   Such as the Doric mothers bore;
And there, perhaps, some seed is sown
The Heracleidan blood might own.

Trust not for freedom to the Franks—
   They have a king who buys and sells;
In native swords, and native ranks,
   The only hope of courage dwells:
But Turkish force, and Latin fraud,
Would break your shield, however broad.

Fill high the bowl with Samian wine!
   Our virgins dance beneath the shade—
I see their glorious black eyes shine;
   But gazing on each glowing maid,
My own the burning tear-drop laves,
To think such breasts must suckle slaves.

Place me on Sunium's marbled steep,
   Where nothing, save the waves and I,
May hear our mutual murmurs sweep;
   There, swan-like, let me sing and die:
A land of slaves shall ne'er be mine—
Dash down yon cup of Samian wine!

LORD BYRON

ODE TO THE WEST WIND

I

O WILD West Wind, thou breath of Autumn's being,
Thou, from whose unseen presence the leaves dead
Are driven, like ghosts from an enchanter fleeing,

Yellow, and black, and pale, and hectic red,
Pestilence-stricken multitudes: O thou,
Who chariotest to their dark wintry bed

The wingéd seeds, where they lie cold and low,
Each like a corpse within its grave, until
Thine azure sister of the spring shall blow

Her clarion o'er the dreaming earth, and fill
(Driving sweet buds like flocks to feed in air)
With living hues and odours plain and hill:

Wild Spirit, which art moving everywhere;
Destroyer and preserver; hear, oh hear!

II

Thou on whose stream, 'mid the steep sky's commotion,
Loose clouds like earth's decaying leaves are shed,
Shook from the tangled boughs of Heaven and Ocean,

Angels of rain and lightning: there are spread
On the blue surface of thine airy surge,
Like the bright hair uplifted from the head

Of some fierce Maenad, even from the dim verge
Of the horizon to the zenith's height,
The locks of the approaching storm. Thou dirge

Of the dying year, to which this closing night
Will be the dome of a vast sepulchre,
Vaulted with all thy congregated might

Of vapours, from whose solid atmosphere
Black rain, and fire, and hail, will burst: oh, hear!

III

Thou who didst waken from his summer dreams
The blue Mediterranean, where he lay
Lulled by the coil of his crystálline streams,

Beside a pumice isle in Baiae's bay,
And saw in sleep old palaces and towers
Quivering within the wave's intenser day,

All overgrown with azure moss and flowers
So sweet, the sense faints picturing them! Thou
For whose path the Atlantic's level powers

Cleave themselves into chasms, while far below
The sea-blooms and the oozy woods which wear
The sapless foliage of the ocean, know

Thy voice, and suddenly grow grey with fear,
And tremble and despoil themselves: oh, hear!

IV

If I were a dead leaf thou mightest bear;
If I were a swift cloud to fly with thee;
A wave to pant beneath thy power, and share

The impulse of thy strength, only less free
Than thou, O uncontrollable! If even
I were as in my boyhood, and could be

The comrade of thy wanderings over Heaven,
As then, when to outstrip thy skiey speed
Scarce seemed a vision; I would ne'er have striven

As thus with thee in prayer in my sore need.
Oh, lift me as a wave, a leaf, a cloud!
I fall upon the thorns of life! I bleed!

A heavy weight of hours has chained and bowed
One too like thee: tameless, and swift, and proud.

V

Make me thy lyre, even as the forest is:
What if my leaves are falling like its own!
The tumult of thy mighty harmonies

Will take from both a deep, autumnal tone,
Sweet though in sadness. Be thou, Spirit fierce,
My spirit! Be thou me, impetuous one!

Drive my dead thoughts over the universe
Like withered leaves to quicken a new birth!
And, by the incantation of this verse,

Scatter, as from an unextinguished hearth
Ashes and sparks, my words among mankind!
Be through my lips to unawakened earth

The trumpet of a prophecy! O, wind,
If Winter comes, can Spring be far behind?

PERCY BYSSHE SHELLEY

OZYMANDIAS

I MET a traveller from an antique land
Who said: Two vast and trunkless legs of stone
Stand in the desert. . . . Near them, on the sand,
Half sunk, a shattered visage lies, whose frown,
And wrinkled lip, and sneer of cold command,
Tell that its sculptor well those passions read
Which yet survive, stamped on these lifeless things,
The hand that mocked them, and the heart that fed:
And on the pedestal these words appear:
'My name is Ozymandias, king of kings:
Look on my works, ye Mighty, and despair!'
Nothing beside remains. Round the decay
Of that colossal wreck, boundless and bare
The lone and level sands stretch far away.

PERCY BYSSHE SHELLEY

NIGHT

SWIFTLY walk o'er the western wave,
        Spirit of Night!
Out of the misty eastern cave,
Where, all the long and lone daylight,
Thou wovest dreams of joy and fear,
Which make thee terrible and dear,—
        Swift be thy flight!

Wrap thy form in a mantle grey,
        Star-inwrought!
Blind with thine hair the eyes of day,
Kiss her until she be wearied out,
Then wander o'er city, and sea, and land,
Touching all with thine opiate wand—
        Come, long-sought!

When I arose and saw the dawn,
        I sighed for thee;
When light rode high, and the dew was gone,
And noon lay heavy on flower and tree,
And the weary Day turned to his rest,
Lingering like an unloved guest,
        I sighed for thee.

Thy brother Death came, and cried,
        Wouldst thou me?
Thy sweet child Sleep, the filmy-eyed,
Murmured like a noontide bee,
Shall I nestle near thy side?
Wouldst thou me?—And I replied,
        No, not thee!

Death will come when thou art dead,
   Soon, too soon—
Sleep will come when thou art fled;
Of neither would I ask the boon
I ask of thee, belovéd Night—
Swift be thine approaching flight,
   Come soon, soon!

PERCY BYSSHE SHELLEY

ON THE SEA

IT keeps eternal whisperings around
 Desolate shores, and with its mighty swell
 Gluts twice ten thousand caverns, till the spell
Of Hecate leaves them their old shadowy sound.
Often 'tis in such gentle temper found,
 That scarcely will the very smallest shell
 Be mov'd for days from where it sometime fell,
When last the winds of heaven were unbound.
Oh ye! who have your eye-balls vex'd and tir'd,
 Feast them upon the wideness of the sea;
  Oh ye! whose ears are dinn'd with uproar rude,
 Or fed too much with cloying melody—
  Sit ye near some old cavern's mouth, and brood
Until ye start, as if the sea-nymphs quir'd!

JOHN KEATS

ON FIRST LOOKING INTO CHAPMAN'S HOMER

MUCH have I travell'd in the realms of gold,
    And many goodly states and kingdoms seen;
  Round many western islands have I been
Which bards in fealty to Apollo hold.
Oft of one wide expanse had I been told
    That deep-brow'd Homer ruled as his demesne;
    Yet did I never breathe its pure serene
Till I heard Chapman speak out loud and bold:
Then felt I like some watcher of the skies
    When a new planet swims into his ken;
Or like stout Cortez when with eagle eyes
    He star'd at the Pacific—and all his men
Look'd at each other with a wild surmise—
    Silent, upon a peak in Darien.

JOHN KEATS

TO SLEEP

O SOFT embalmer of the still midnight!
  Shutting, with careful fingers and benign,
Our gloom-pleas'd eyes, embower'd from the light,
  Enshaded in forgetfulness divine:
O soothest sleep! if so it please thee, close,
  In midst of this thine hymn, my willing eyes,
Or wait the 'Amen', ere thy poppy throws
  Around my bed its lulling charities;
Then save me, or the passéd day will shine
Upon my pillow, breeding many woes,—
  Save me from curious conscience, that still lords
Its strength for darkness, burrowing like a mole;
  Turn the key deftly in the oiléd wards,
And seal the hushéd casket of my soul.

JOHN KEATS

ODE TO A NIGHTINGALE

My heart aches, and a drowsy numbness pains
   My sense, as though of hemlock I had drunk,
Or emptied some dull opiate to the drains
   One minute past, and Lethé-wards had sunk:
'Tis not through envy of thy happy lot,
   But being too happy in thine happiness,—
      That thou, light-wingéd Dryad of the trees,
         In some melodious plot
     Of beechen green, and shadows numberless,
      Singest of summer in full-throated ease.

O, for a draught of vintage! that hath been
   Cool'd a long age in the deep-delvéd earth,
Tasting of Flora and the country green,
   Dance, and Provençal song, and sunburnt mirth!
O for a beaker full of the warm South,
   Full of the true, the blushful Hippocrene,
      With beaded bubbles winking at the brim,
         And purple-stainéd mouth;
     That I might drink, and leave the world unseen,
      And with thee fade away into the forest dim:

Fade far away, dissolve, and quite forget
   What thou among the leaves hast never known,
The weariness, the fever, and the fret
   Here, where men sit and hear each other groan;
Where palsy shakes a few, sad, last gray hairs,
   Where youth grows pale, and spectre-thin, and dies;

Where but to think is to be full of sorrow
And leaden-eyed despairs,
Where Beauty cannot keep her lustrous eyes,
Or new Love pine at them beyond to-morrow.

Away! away! for I will fly to thee,
Not charioted by Bacchus and his pards,
But on the viewless wings of Poesy,
Though the dull brain perplexes and retards:
Already with thee! tender is the night,
And haply the Queen-Moon is on her throne,
Cluster'd around by all her starry Fays;
But here there is no light,
Save what from heaven is with the breezes blown
Through verdurous glooms and winding mossy ways.

I cannot see what flowers are at my feet,
Nor what soft incense hangs upon the boughs,
But, in embalmèd darkness, guess each sweet
Wherewith the seasonable month endows
The grass, the thicket, and the fruit-tree wild;
White hawthorn, and the pastoral eglantine;
Fast fading violets cover'd up in leaves;
And mid-May's eldest child,
The coming musk-rose, full of dewy wine,
The murmurous haunt of flies on summer eves.

Darkling I listen; and, for many a time
I have been half in love with easeful Death,
Call'd him soft names in many a musèd rhyme,
To take into the air my quiet breath;

Now more than ever seems it rich to die,
  To cease upon the midnight with no pain,
    While thou art pouring forth thy soul abroad
      In such an ecstasy!
Still wouldst thou sing, and I have ears in vain—
  To thy high requiem become a sod.

Thou wast not born for death, immortal Bird!
  No hungry generations tread thee down;
The voice I hear this passing night was heard
  In ancient days by emperor and clown:
Perhaps the self-same song that found a path
    Through the sad heart of Ruth, when, sick for home,
      She stood in tears amid the alien corn;
        The same that oft-times hath
Charm'd magic casements, opening on the foam
  Of perilous seas, in faery lands forlorn.

Forlorn! the very word is like a bell
  To toll me back from thee to my sole self!
Adieu! the fancy cannot cheat so well
  As she is fam'd to do, deceiving elf.
Adieu! adieu! thy plaintive anthem fades
  Past the near meadows, over the still stream,
    Up the hill-side; and now 'tis buried deep
      In the next valley-glades:
Was it a vision, or a waking dream?
  Fled is that music:—Do I wake or sleep?

JOHN KEATS

A JACOBITE'S EPITAPH

To my true king I offer'd free from stain
Courage and faith; vain faith, and courage vain.
For him I threw lands, honours, wealth, away,
And one dear hope, that was more prized than they.
For him I languish'd in a foreign clime,
Gray-hair'd with sorrow in my manhood's prime;
Heard on Lavernia Scargill's whispering trees,
And pined by Arno for my lovelier Tees;
Beheld each night my home in fever'd sleep,
Each morning started from the dream to weep;
Till God, who saw me tried too sorely, gave
The resting-place I ask'd, an early grave.
O thou, whom chance leads to this nameless stone
From that proud country which was once mine own,
By those white cliffs I never more must see,
By that dear language which I spake like thee,
Forget all feuds, and shed one English tear
O'er English dust. A broken heart lies here.

LORD MACAULAY

NASEBY

Oh, wherefore come ye forth, in triumph from the
   North,
   With your hands, and your feet, and your raiment all
   red?
And wherefore doth your rout send forth a joyous shout?
   And whence be the grapes of the winepress which ye
   tread?

Oh, evil was the root, and bitter was the fruit,
   And crimson was the juice of the vintage that we
   trod;
For we trampled on the throng of the haughty and the
   strong,
   Who sate in the high places, and slew the saints of God.

It was about the noon of a glorious day of June
   That we saw their banners dance and their cuirasses
   shine;
And the Man of Blood was there, with his long essenced
   hair,
   And Astley, and Sir Marmaduke, and Rupert of the
   Rhine.

Like a servant of the Lord, with his Bible and his sword,
   The General rode along us to form us for the fight,
When a murmuring sound broke out, and swelled into a
   shout,
   Among the godless horsemen upon the tyrant's right.

And hark! like the roar of the billows on the shore,
  The cry of battle rises along their charging line!
For God! for the Cause! for the Church! for the Laws!
  For Charles, King of England, and Rupert of the
    Rhine!

The furious German comes, with his clarions and his
    drums,
  His bravoes of Alsatia and pages of Whitehall;
They are bursting on our flanks. Grasp your pikes—
    close your ranks;
  For Rupert never comes but to conquer or to fall.

They are here!—They rush on! We are broken—We
    are gone!
  Our left is borne before them like stubble on the blast.
O Lord, put forth thy might! O Lord, defend the right!
  Stand back to back, in God's name, and fight it to the
    last.

Stout Skippon hath a wound; the centre hath given
    ground:
  Hark! hark! what means the trampling of horsemen
    on our rear?
Whose banner do I see, boys? 'Tis he, thank God, 'tis he,
    boys!—
  Bear up another minute! brave Oliver is here.

Their heads all stooping low, their points all in a row,
  Like a whirlwind on the trees, like a deluge on the
    dykes,
Our cuirassiers have burst on the ranks of the Accurst,
  And at a shock have scattered the forest of his pikes.

Fast, fast, the gallants ride, in some safe nook to hide
  Their coward heads, predestined to rot on Temple
    Bar;
And he—he turns, he flies; shame on those cruel eyes
  That bore to look on torture, and dare not look on
    war.

Ho! comrades, scour the plain; and, ere ye strip the
    slain,
  First give another stab to make your quest secure,
Then shake from sleeves and pockets their broad-pieces[1]
    and lockets,
  The tokens of the wanton, the plunder of the poor.

Fools! your doublets shone with gold, and your hearts
    were gay and bold,
  When you kissed your lily hands to your lemans[2] to-
    day;
And to-morrow shall the fox, from her chambers in the
    rocks,
  Lead forth her tawny cubs to howl above the prey.

---

[1] gold coins   [2] lady-loves

Where be your tongues that late mocked at heaven and
 hell and fate,
 And the fingers that once were so busy with your
  blades,
Your perfumed satin clothes, your catches[1] and your
 oaths,
 Your stage-plays, and your sonnets, your diamonds
  and your spades?

Down, down, for ever down, with the mitre and the
 crown,
 With the Belial of the Court and the Mammon of the
  Pope;
There is woe in Oxford Halls; there is wail in Durham's
 Stalls!
 The Jesuit smites his bosom; the Bishop rends his
  cope.

And She of the Seven Hills shall mourn her children's
 ills,
 And tremble when she thinks on the edge of England's
  sword;
And the Kings of earth in fear shall shudder when they
 hear
 What the hand of God hath wrought for the Houses
  and the Word.

LORD MACAULAY

[1] part-songs

HYMN OF THE MORAVIAN NUNS OF BETHLEHEM
at the consecration of Pulaski's banner

WHEN the dying flame of day
   Through the chancel shot its ray,
Far the glimmering tapers shed
Faint light on the cowléd head;
And the censer burning swung,
Where, before the altar, hung
The crimson banner, that with prayer
Had been consecrated there.
And the nuns' sweet hymn was heard the while,
Sung low, in the dim, mysterious aisle.

  'Take thy banner! May it wave
Proudly o'er the good and brave;
When the battle's distant wail
Breaks the sabbath of our vale;
When the clarion's music thrills
To the hearts of these lone hills,
When the spear in conflict shakes,
And the strong lance shivering breaks.

  'Take thy banner! and, beneath
The battle-cloud's encircling wreath,
Guard it, till our homes are free!
Guard it! God will prosper thee!
In the dark and trying hour,
In the breaking forth of power,
In the rush of steeds and men,
His right hand will shield thee then.

'Take thy banner! But when night
Closes round the ghastly fight,
If the vanquished warrior bow,
Spare him! By our holy vow,
By our prayers and many tears,
By the mercy that endears,
Spare him! he our love hath shared!
Spare him! as thou wouldst be spared!

'Take thy banner! and if e'er
Thou shouldst press the soldier's bier,
And the muffled drum should beat
To the tread of mournful feet,
Then this crimson flag shall be
Martial cloak and shroud for thee.'

The warrior took that banner proud,
And it was his martial cloak and shroud!

HENRY WADSWORTH LONGFELLOW

FROM 'DREAM–PEDLARY'

IF there were dreams to sell,
  What would you buy?
Some cost a passing bell;
  Some a light sigh,
That shakes from Life's fresh crown
Only a rose leaf down.
If there were dreams to sell,
Merry and sad to tell,
And the crier rung the bell,
  What would you buy?

A cottage lone and still,
  With bowers nigh,
Shadowy, my woes to still,
  Until I die.
Such pearl from Life's fresh crown
Fain would I shake me down.
Were dreams to have at will,
This would best heal my ill,
  This would I buy.

THOMAS LOVELL BEDDOES

TO HELEN

HELEN, thy beauty is to me
   Like those Nicéan[1] barks of yore
That gently, o'er a perfumed sea,
   The weary way-worn wanderer bore
   To his own native shore.

On desperate seas long wont to roam,
   Thy hyacinth hair, thy classic face,
Thy Naiad airs have brought me home
   To the glory that was Greece,
And the grandeur that was Rome.

Lo, in yon brilliant window-niche
   How statue-like I see thee stand,
   The agate lamp within thy hand,
Ah! Psyche, from the regions which
   Are Holy Land!

EDGAR ALLAN POE

[1] Of Nicaea in Bithynia, whence Catullus sailed, homesick, back to Italy

FROM 'THE RUBÁIYÁT OF OMAR KHAYYÁM'

AWAKE! for Morning in the Bowl of Night
  Has flung the Stone that puts the Stars to Flight:
    And lo! the Hunter of the East has caught
The Sultán's Turret in a Noose of Light.

Irám indeed is gone with all its Rose,
And Jamshýd's Sev'n-ring'd Cup where no one knows;
    But still the Vine her ancient Ruby yields,
And still a Garden by the Water blows.

Come, fill the Cup, and in the Fire of Spring
The Winter Garment of Repentance fling:
    The Bird of Time has but a little way
To fly—and Lo! the Bird is on the Wing.

Here with a Loaf of Bread beneath the Bough,
A Flask of Wine, a Book of Verse—and Thou
    Beside me singing in the Wilderness—
And Wilderness is Paradise enow.

Think, in this battered Caravanserai
Whose Doorways are alternate Night and Day,
    How Sultán after Sultán with his Pomp
Abode his Hour or two, and went his way.

I sometimes think that never blows so red
The Rose as where some buried Caesar bled:
   That every Hyacinth the Garden wears
Dropt in its Lap from some once lovely Head.

Ah, my Belovèd, fill the cup that clears
To-DAY of past Regrets and future Fears—
   To-morrow?—Why, To-morrow I may be
Myself with Yesterday's Sev'n Thousand Years.

Alike for those who for To-DAY prepare,
And those that after a To-MORROW stare,
   A Muezzín from the Tower of Darkness cries,
'Fools! your Reward is neither Here nor There!'

Myself when young did eagerly frequent
Doctor and Saint, and heard great Argument
   About it and about, but evermore
Came out by the same Door as in I went.

Ah, fill the Cup:—what boots it to repeat
How time is slipping underneath our Feet:
   Unborn To-MORROW and dead YESTERDAY,
Why fret about them if To-DAY be sweet!

The Moving Finger writes; and, having writ,
Moves on; nor all your Piety nor Wit
   Shall lure it back to cancel half a line,
Nor all your Tears wash out a word of it.

Ah, with the Grape my fading Life provide,
And wash my Body whence the Life has died,
    And in a Winding-sheet of Vine-leaf wrapt,
So bury me by some sweet Garden side.

Alas, that Spring should vanish with the Rose!
That Youth's sweet-scented Manuscript should close!
    The Nightingale that in the branches sang,
Ah, whence, and whither flown again, who knows?

Oh Love! could you and I with Fate conspire
To grasp this sorry Scheme of Things entire,
    Would not we shatter it to bits—and then
Re-mould it nearer to the Heart's Desire!

EDWARD FITZGERALD

A FAREWELL

FLOW down, cold rivulet, to the sea,
    Thy tribute wave deliver:
No more by thee my steps shall be,
    For ever and for ever.

Flow, softly flow, by lawn and lea,
    A rivulet then a river:
No where by thee my steps shall be,
    For ever and for ever.

But here will sigh thine alder tree,
    And here thine aspen shiver;
And here by thee will hum the bee,
    For ever and for ever.

A thousand suns will stream on thee,
    A thousand moons will quiver;
But not by thee my steps shall be,
    For ever and for ever.

LORD TENNYSON

FRATER AVE ATQUE VALE

Row us out from Desenzano, to your Sirmione row!
  So they row'd, and there we landed—'O venusta[1]
Sirmio!'
There to me thro' all the groves of olive in the summer
  glow,
There beneath the Roman ruin where the purple
  flowers grow,
Came that 'Ave atque Vale'[2] of the Poet's hopeless woe,
Tenderest of Roman poets nineteen-hundred years ago,
'Frater Ave atque Vale'—as we wander'd to and fro
Gazing at the Lydian laughter of the Garda Lake
  below,
Sweet Catullus' all-but-island, olive-silvery Sirmio!

LORD TENNYSON

[1] beautiful   [2] 'Hail and Farewell'

THREE SONGS FROM 'THE PRINCESS'

i

THE splendour falls on castle walls
    And snowy summits old in story:
The long light shakes across the lakes,
    And the wild cataract leaps in glory.
Blow, bugle, blow, set the wild echoes flying,
Blow, bugle; answer, echoes, dying, dying, dying.

O hark, O hear! how thin and clear,
    And thinner, clearer, farther going!
O sweet and far from cliff and scar
    The horns of Elfland faintly blowing!
Blow, let us hear the purple glens replying:
Blow, bugle; answer, echoes, dying, dying, dying.

O love, they die in yon rich sky,
    They faint on hill or field or river:
Our echoes roll from soul to soul,
    And grow for ever and for ever.
Blow, bugle, blow, set the wild echoes flying,
And answer, echoes, answer, dying, dying, dying.

ii

Now sleeps the crimson petal, now the white;
 Nor waves the cypress in the palace walk;
Nor winks the gold fin in the porphyry font:
The fire-fly wakens: waken thou with me.

Now droops the milkwhite peacock like a ghost,
And like a ghost she glimmers on to me.

Now lies the earth all Danaë to the stars,
And all thy heart lies open unto me.

Now slides the silent meteor on, and leaves
A shining furrow, as thy thoughts in me.

Now folds the lily all her sweetness up,
And slips into the bosom of the lake:
So fold thyself, my dearest, thou, and slip
Into my bosom and be lost in me.

iii

Come down, O maid, from yonder mountain height:
 What pleasure lives in height (the shepherd sang)
In height and cold, the splendour of the hills?
But cease to move so near the Heavens, and cease
To glide a sunbeam by the blasted Pine,
To sit a star upon the sparkling spire;
And come, for Love is of the valley, come,
For Love is of the valley, come thou down

And find him; by the happy threshold, he,
Or hand in hand with Plenty in the maize,
Or red with spirted purple of the vats,
Or foxlike in the vine; nor cares to walk
With Death and Morning on the silver horns,
Nor wilt thou snare him in the white ravine,
Nor find him dropt upon the firths of ice,
That huddling slant in furrow-cloven falls
To roll the torrent out of dusky doors:
But follow; let the torrent dance thee down
To find him in the valley; let the wild
Lean-headed Eagles yelp alone, and leave
The monstrous ledges there to slope, and spill
Their thousand wreaths of dangling water-smoke,
That like a broken purpose waste in air:
So waste not thou; but come; for all the vales
Await thee; azure pillars of the hearth
Arise to thee; the children call, and I
Thy shepherd pipe, and sweet is every sound,
Sweeter thy voice, but every sound is sweet;
Myriads of rivulets hurrying thro' the lawn,
The moan of doves in immemorial elms,
And murmuring of innumerable bees.

LORD TENNYSON

THE REVENGE

A Ballad of the Fleet

At Florés in the Azores Sir Richard Grenville lay,
And a pinnace, like a fluttered bird, came flying
from far away:
'Spanish ships of war at sea! we have sighted fifty-three!'
Then sware Lord Thomas Howard: ''Fore God I am
no coward;
But I cannot meet them here, for my ships are out of
gear,
And the half my men are sick. I must fly, but follow
quick.
We are six ships of the line; can we fight with fifty-three?'

Then spake Sir Richard Grenville: 'I know you are no
coward;
You fly them for a moment to fight with them again.
But I've ninety men and more that are lying sick ashore.
I should count myself the coward if I left them, my Lord
Howard,
To these Inquisition dogs and the devildoms of Spain.'

So Lord Howard passed away with five ships of war
that day,
Till he melted like a cloud in the silent summer heaven;
But Sir Richard bore in hand all his sick men from the
land
Very carefully and slow,
Men of Bideford in Devon,
And we laid them on the ballast down below;

For we brought them all aboard,

And they blest him in their pain, that they were not left
to Spain,

To the thumbscrew and the stake, for the glory of the
Lord.

He had only a hundred seamen to work the ship and to
fight,

And he sailed away from Florés till the Spaniard came
in sight,

With his huge sea-castles heaving upon the weather
bow.

'Shall we fight or shall we fly?

Good Sir Richard, tell us now,

For to fight is but to die!

There'll be little of us left by the time this sun be set.'

And Sir Richard said again: 'We be all good English
men.

Let us bang those dogs of Seville, the children of the
devil,

For I never turned my back upon Don or devil yet.'

Sir Richard spoke and he laughed, and we roared a
hurrah, and so

The little Revenge ran on sheer into the heart of the foe,

With her hundred fighters on deck, and her ninety sick
below;

For half their fleet to the right and half to the left were
seen,

And the little Revenge ran on through the long sea-
lane between.

Thousands of their soldiers looked down from their
    decks and laughed.
Thousands of their seamen made mock at the mad little
    craft
Running on and on, till delayed
By their mountain-like San Philip that, of fifteen hun-
    dred tons,
And up-shadowing high above us with her yawning
    tiers of guns,
Took the breath from our sails, and we stayed.

And while now the great San Philip hung above us like
    a cloud
Whence the thunderbolt will fall
Long and loud,
Four galleons drew away
From the Spanish fleet that day,
And two upon the larboard and two upon the star-
    board lay,
And the battle thunder broke from them all.

But anon the great San Philip, she bethought herself
    and went,
Having that within her womb that had left her ill content;
And the rest they came aboard us, and they fought us
    hand to hand,
For a dozen times they came with their pikes and mus-
    queteers,
And a dozen times we shook 'em off as a dog that
    shakes his ears
When he leaps from the water to the land.

And the sun went down, and the stars came out far
    over the summer sea,
But never a moment ceased the fight of the one and the
    fifty-three.
Ship after ship, the whole night long, their high-built
    galleons came,
Ship after ship, the whole night long, with her battle-
    thunder and flame;
Ship after ship, the whole night long, drew back with
    her dead and her shame.
For some were sunk and many were shattered, and so
    could fight us no more—
God of battles, was ever a battle like this in the world
    before?

For he said, 'Fight on! fight on!'
Though his vessel was all but a wreck;
And it chanced that, when half of the short summer
    night was gone,
With a grisly wound to be drest he had left the deck,
But a bullet struck him that was dressing it suddenly
    dead,
And himself he was wounded again in the side and the
    head,
And he said, 'Fight on! fight on!'

And the night went down and the sun smiled out far
    over the summer sea,
And the Spanish fleet with broken sides lay round us
    all in a ring;

But they dared not touch us again, for they feared that
    we still could sting,
So they watched what the end would be.
And we had not fought them in vain,
But in perilous plight were we,
Seeing forty of our poor hundred were slain,
And half of the rest of us maimed for life
In the crash of the cannonades and the desperate strife;
And the sick men down in the hold were most of them
    stark and cold,
And the pikes were all broken or bent, and the powder
    was all of it spent;
And the masts and the rigging were lying over the side;
But Sir Richard cried in his English pride,
'We have fought such a fight for a day and a night
As may never be fought again!
We have won great glory, my men!
And a day less or more
At sea or ashore,
We die—does it matter when?
Sink me the ship, Master Gunner—sink her, split her
    in twain!
Fall into the hands of God, not into the hands of
    Spain!'

And the gunner said, 'Ay, ay,' but the seamen made reply:
'We have children, we have wives,
And the Lord hath spared our lives.
We will make the Spaniard promise, if we yield, to let
    us go;

We shall live to fight again and to strike another blow.'
And the lion there lay dying, and they yielded to the
    foe.

And the stately Spanish men to their flagship bore him
    then,
Where they laid him by the mast, old Sir Richard
    caught at last,
And they praised him to his face with their courtly
    foreign grace;
But he rose upon their decks, and he cried:
'I have fought for Queen and Faith like a valiant man
    and true;
I have only done my duty as a man is bound to do;
With a joyful spirit I Sir Richard Grenville die!'
And he fell upon their decks, and he died.

And they stared at the dead that had been so valiant
    and true,
And had holden the power and glory of Spain so
    cheap
That he dared her with one little ship and his English
    few;
Was he devil or man? He was devil for aught they
    knew,
But they sank his body with honour down into the
    deep,
And they manned the Revenge with a swarthier alien
    crew,
And away she sailed with her loss and longed for her
    own;

When a wind from the lands they had ruined awoke
    from sleep,
And the water began to heave and the weather to
    moan,
And or ever that evening ended a great gale blew,
And a wave like the wave that is raised by an earth-
    quake grew,
Till it smote on their hulls and their sails and their
    masts and their flags,
And the whole sea plunged and fell on the shot-shattered
    navy of Spain,
And the little Revenge herself went down by the island
    crags
To be lost evermore in the main.

                                        LORD TENNYSON

ULYSSES

IT little profits that an idle king,
    By this still hearth, among these barren crags,
Match'd with an aged wife, I mete and dole
Unequal laws unto a savage race,
That hoard, and sleep, and feed, and know not me.
I cannot rest from travel: I will drink
Life to the lees: all times I have enjoy'd
Greatly, have suffer'd greatly, both with those
That loved me, and alone; on shore, and when
Thro' scudding drifts the rainy Hyades
Vext the dim sea: I am become a name;
For always roaming with a hungry heart
Much have I seen and known; cities of men
And manners, climates, councils, governments,

Myself not least, but honour'd of them all;
And drunk delight of battle with my peers,
Far on the ringing plains of windy Troy.
I am a part of all that I have met;
Yet all experience is an arch wherethro'
Gleams that untravell'd world, whose margin fades
For ever and for ever when I move.
How dull it is to pause, to make an end,
To rust unburnish'd, not to shine in use!
As tho' to breathe were life. Life piled on life
Were all too little, and of one to me
Little remains: but every hour is saved
From that eternal silence, something more,
A bringer of new things; and vile it were
For some three suns to store and hoard myself,
And this grey spirit yearning in desire
To follow knowledge, like a sinking star,
Beyond the utmost bound of human thought.

This is my son, mine own Telemachus,
To whom I leave the sceptre and the isle—
Well-loved of me, discerning to fulfil
This labour, by slow prudence to make mild
A rugged people, and thro' soft degrees
Subdue them to the useful and the good.
Most blameless is he, centred in the sphere
Of common duties, decent not to fail
In offices of tenderness, and pay
Meet adoration to my household gods,
When I am gone. He works his work, I mine.

There lies the port: the vessel puffs her sail:
There gloom the dark broad seas. My mariners,
Souls that have toil'd, and wrought, and thought
    with me—
That ever with a frolic welcome took
The thunder and the sunshine, and opposed
Free hearts, free foreheads—you and I are old;
Old age hath yet his honour and his toil;
Death closes all: but something ere the end,
Some work of noble note, may yet be done,
Not unbecoming men that strove with Gods.
The lights begin to twinkle from the rocks:
The long day wanes: the slow moon climbs: the deep
Moans round with many voices. Come, my friends,
'Tis not too late to seek a newer world.
Push off, and, sitting well in order, smite
The sounding furrows; for my purpose holds
To sail beyond the sunset, and the baths
Of all the western stars, until I die.
It may be that the gulfs will wash us down:
It may be we shall touch the Happy Isles,
And see the great Achilles, whom we knew.
Tho' much is taken, much abides; and tho'
We are not now that strength which in old days
Moved earth and heaven; that which we are, we are;
One equal temper of heroic hearts,
Made weak by time and fate, but strong in will
To strive, to seek, to find, and not to yield.

LORD TENNYSON

FROM 'THE PASSING OF ARTHUR'

Sir Bedivere tells the story of the last battle of King Arthur. He is fighting against a revolt led by his nephew Modred.

So all day long the noise of battle roll'd
Among the mountains by the winter sea;
Until King Arthur's Table, man by man,
Had fall'n in Lyonnesse about their lord,
King Arthur. Then, because his wound was deep,
The bold Sir Bedivere uplifted him,
And bore him to a chapel nigh the field,
A broken chancel with a broken cross,
That stood on a dark strait of barren land:
On one side lay the Ocean, and on one
Lay a great water, and the moon was full.

Then spake King Arthur to Sir Bedivere;
'The sequel of to-day unsolders all
The goodliest fellowship of famous knights
Whereof this world holds record. Such a sleep
They sleep—the men I loved. I think that we
Shall never more, at any future time,
Delight our souls with talk of knightly deeds,
Walking about the gardens and the halls
Of Camelot, as in the days that were.
I perish by this people which I made,—
Tho' Merlin sware that I should come again
To rule once more; but, let what will be, be,
I am so deeply smitten thro' the helm
That without help I cannot last till morn.

Thou therefore take my brand Excalibur,
Which was my pride: for thou rememberest how
In those old days, one summer noon, an arm
Rose up from out the bosom of the lake,
Clothed in white samite, mystic, wonderful,
Holding the sword—and how I row'd across
And took it, and have worn it, like a king;
And, wheresoever I am sung or told
In aftertime, this also shall be known:
But now delay not: take Excalibur,
And fling him far into the middle mere:
Watch what thou seëst, and lightly bring me word.'

.   .   .   .

Then quickly rose Sir Bedivere, and ran,
And, leaping down the ridges lightly, plunged
Among the bulrush beds, and clutch'd the sword,
And strongly wheel'd and threw it. The great brand
Made lightnings in the splendour of the moon,
And flashing round and round, and whirl'd in an arch,
Shot like a streamer of the northern morn,
Seen where the moving isles of winter shock
By night, with noises of the Northern Sea.
So flash'd and fell the brand Excalibur:
But ere he dipt the surface, rose an arm
Clothed in white samite, mystic, wonderful,
And caught him by the hilt, and brandish'd him
Three times, and drew him under in the mere.
And lightly went the other to the King.

.   .   .   .

And answer made King Arthur, breathing hard:
'My end draws nigh; 'tis time that I were gone.

Make broad thy shoulders to receive my weight,
And bear me to the margin; yet I fear
My wound hath taken cold, and I shall die.'

So saying, from the pavement he half rose,
Slowly, with pain, reclining on his arm,
And looking wistfully with wide blue eyes
As in a picture. Him Sir Bedivere
Remorsefully regarded thro' his tears,
And would have spoken, but he found not words;
Then took with care, and kneeling on one knee,
O'er both his shoulders drew the languid hands,
And rising bore him thro' the place of tombs.

But, as he walked, King Arthur panted hard,
Like one that feels a nightmare on his bed
When all the house is mute. So sigh'd the King,
Muttering and murmuring at his ear, 'Quick, quick!
I fear it is too late, and I shall die.'
But the other swiftly strode from ridge to ridge,
Clothed with his breath, and looking, as he walk'd,
Larger than human on the frozen hills.
He heard the deep behind him, and a cry
Before. His own thought drove him like a goad.
Dry clash'd his harness in the icy caves
And barren chasms, and all to left and right
The bare black cliff clang'd round him, as he based
His feet on juts of slippery crag that rang
Sharp-smitten with the dint of arméd heels—
And on a sudden, lo! the level lake,
And the long glories of the winter moon.

Then saw they how there hove a dusky barge,
Dark as a funeral scarf from stem to stern,
Beneath them; and descending they were ware
That all the decks were dense with stately forms,
Black-stoled, black-hooded, like a dream—by these
Three Queens with crowns of gold: and from them rose
A cry that shiver'd to the tingling stars,
And, as it were one voice, an agony
Of lamentation, like a wind that shrills
All night in a waste land, where no one comes,
Or hath come, since the making of the world.

Then murmur'd Arthur, 'Place me in the barge.'
So to the barge they came. There those three Queens
Put forth their hands, and took the King, and wept.
But she, that rose the tallest of them all
And fairest, laid his head upon her lap,
And loosed the shatter'd casque, and chafed his hands,
And call'd him by his name, complaining loud
And dropping bitter tears against a brow
Striped with dark blood: for all his face was white
And colourless, and like the wither'd moon
Smote by the fresh beam of the springing east;
And all his greaves and cuisses[1] dash'd with drops
Of onset; and the light and lustrous curls—
That made his forehead like a rising sun
High from the daïs-throne—were parch'd with dust;
Or, clotted into points and hanging loose,
Mix'd with the knightly growth that fringed his lips.
So like a shatter'd column lay the King;

[1] thigh-pieces

Not like that Arthur who, with lance in rest,
From spur to plume a star of tournament,
Shot thro' the lists at Camelot, and charged
Before the eyes of ladies and of kings.

    Then loudly cried the bold Sir Bedivere:
'Ah! my Lord Arthur, whither shall I go?
Where shall I hide my forehead and my eyes?
For now I see the true old times are dead,
When every morning brought a noble chance,
And every chance brought out a noble knight.
Such times have been not since the light that led
The holy Elders with the gift of myrrh.
But now the whole Round Table is dissolved
Which was an image of the mighty world,
And I, the last, go forth companionless,
And the days darken round me, and the years,
Among new men, strange faces, other minds.'

    And slowly answer'd Arthur from the barge:
'The old order changeth, yielding place to new,
And God fulfils himself in many ways,
Lest one good custom should corrupt the world.
Comfort thyself: what comfort is in me?
I have lived my life, and that which I have done
May He within himself make pure! but thou,
If thou shouldst never see my face again,
Pray for my soul. More things are wrought by prayer
Than this world dreams of. Wherefore, let thy voice
Rise like a fountain for me night and day.
For what are men better than sheep or goats

That nourish a blind life within the brain,
If, knowing God, they lift not hands of prayer
Both for themselves and those who call them friend?
For so the whole round earth is every way
Bound by gold chains about the feet of God.
But now farewell. I am going a long way
With these thou seëst—if indeed I go
(For all my mind is clouded with a doubt)—
To the island-valley of Avilion;
Where falls not hail, or rain, or any snow,
Nor ever wind blows loudly: but it lies
Deep-meadow'd, happy, fair with orchard lawns
And bowery hollows crown'd with summer sea,
Where I will heal me of my grievous wound.'

So said he, and the barge with oar and sail
Moved from the brink, like some full-breasted swan
That, fluting a wild carol ere her death,
Ruffles her pure cold plume, and takes the flood
With swarthy webs. Long stood Sir Bedivere
Revolving many memories, till the hull
Look'd one black dot against the verge of dawn,
And on the mere the wailing died away.

But when that moan had past for evermore,
The stillness of the dead world's winter dawn
Amazed him, and he groan'd, 'The King is gone.'
And therewithal came on him the weird rhyme,
'From the great deep to the great deep he goes.'

Whereat he slowly turn'd and slowly clomb
The last hard footstep of that iron crag;
Thence mark'd the black hull moving yet, and cried.
'He passes to be King among the dead,
And after healing of his grievous wound
He comes again; but—if he comes no more—
O me, be yon dark Queens in yon black boat,
Who shriek'd and wail'd, the three whereat we gazed
On that high day, when, clothed with living light,
They stood before his throne in silence, friends
Of Arthur, who should help him at his need?'

Then from the dawn it seem'd there came, but faint
As from beyond the limit of the world,
Like the last echo born of a great cry,
Sounds, as if some fair city were one voice
Around a king returning from his wars.

Thereat once more he moved about, and clomb
Ev'n to the highest he could climb, and saw,
Straining his eyes beneath an arch of hand,
Or thought he saw, the speck that bare the King,
Down that long water opening on the deep
Somewhere far off, pass on and on, and go
From less to less and vanish into light.
And the new sun rose bringing the new year.

LORD TENNYSON

BREAK, BREAK, BREAK

BREAK, break, break,
  On thy cold grey stones, O Sea!
And I would that my tongue could utter
  The thoughts that arise in me.

O well for the fisherman's boy,
  That he shouts with his sister at play!
O well for the sailor lad,
  That he sings in his boat on the bay!

And the stately ships go on
  To their haven under the hill;
But O for the touch of a vanish'd hand,
  And the sound of a voice that is still!

Break, break, break,
  At the foot of thy crags, O Sea!
But the tender grace of a day that is dead
  Will never come back to me.

LORD TENNYSON

CROSSING THE BAR

SUNSET and evening star,
    And one clear call for me!
And may there be no moaning of the bar,
    When I put out to sea,

But such a tide as moving seems asleep,
    Too full for sound and foam,
When that which drew from out the boundless deep
    Turns again home.

Twilight and evening bell,
    And after that the dark!
And may there be no sadness of farewell,
    When I embark;

For tho' from out our bourne of Time and Place
    The flood may bear me far,
I hope to see my Pilot face to face
    When I have crost the bar.

LORD TENNYSON

HOME THOUGHTS, FROM ABROAD

OH, to be in England
  Now that April's there,
And whoever wakes in England
Sees, some morning, unaware,
That the lowest boughs and the brushwood sheaf
Round the elm-tree bole are in tiny leaf,
While the chaffinch sings on the orchard bough,
In England—now.

And after April, when May follows,
And the whitethroat builds, and all the swallows,
Hark! where my blossomed pear-tree in the hedge
Leans to the field and scatters on the clover
Blossoms and dewdrops—at the bent spray's edge—
That's the wise thrush; he sings each song twice over,
Lest you should think he never could recapture
The first fine careless rapture!
And though the fields look rough with hoary dew,
All will be gay when noontide wakes anew
The buttercups, the little children's dower,
—Far brighter than this gaudy melon-flower!

ROBERT BROWNING

CAVALIER SONG

KENTISH Sir Byng stood for his King,
Bidding the crop-headed Parliament swing;
And, pressing a troop unable to stoop
And see the rogues flourish and honest[1] folk droop,
Marched them along, fifty-score strong,
Great-hearted gentlemen, singing this song.

God for King Charles! Pym and such carles[2]
To the Devil that prompts 'em their treasonous parles[3]!
Cavaliers, up! Lips from the cup,
Hands from the pasty, nor bite take nor sup
Till you're—
    CHORUS.—*Marching along, fifty-score strong,*
            Great-hearted gentlemen singing this song.

Hampden to hell, and his obsequies' knell
Serve Hazelrig, Fiennes, and young Harry as well!
England, good cheer! Rupert is near!
Kentish and loyalists, keep we not here
    CHORUS.—*Marching along, fifty-score strong,*
            Great-hearted gentlemen, singing this song?

Then, God for King Charles! Pym and his snarls
To the Devil that pricks on such pestilent carles!
Hold by the right, you double your might;
So, onward to Nottingham, fresh for the fight,
    CHORUS.—*March we along, fifty-score strong,*
            Great-hearted gentlemen, singing this song!

ROBERT BROWNING

[1] loyal   [2] low-bred men   [3] speeches

MEETING AT NIGHT

THE grey sea and the long black land;
And the yellow half-moon large and low;
And the startled little waves that leap
In fiery ringlets from their sleep,
As I gain the cove with pushing prow,
And quench its speed in the slushy sand.

Then a mile of warm sea-scented beach;
Three fields to cross till a farm appears;
A tap at the pane, the quick sharp scratch
And blue spurt of a lighted match,
And a voice less loud, thro' its joys and fears,
Than the two hearts beating each to each!

ROBERT BROWNING

PARTING AT MORNING

ROUND the cape of a sudden came the sea,
And the sun looked over the mountain's rim:
And straight was a path of gold for him,
And the need of a world of men for me.

ROBERT BROWNING

THE LOST LEADER

Just for a handful of silver he left us,
    Just for a riband to stick in his coat—
Found the one gift of which fortune bereft us,
    Lost all the others she lets us devote;
They, with the gold to give, doled him out silver,
    So much was theirs who so little allowed:
How all our copper had gone for his service!
    Rags—were they purple, his heart had been proud!
We that had loved him so, followed him, honoured him,
    Lived in his mild and magnificent eye,
Learned his great language, caught his clear accents,
    Made him our pattern to live and to die!
Shakespeare was of us, Milton was for us,
    Burns, Shelley, were with us,—they watch from their
        graves!
He alone breaks from the van and the freemen,
    He alone sinks to the rear and the slaves!

We shall march prospering,—not thro' his presence;
    Songs may inspirit us,—not from his lyre;
Deeds will be done,—while he boasts his quiescence,
    Still bidding crouch whom the rest bade aspire:
Blot out his name, then, record one lost soul more,
    One task more declined, one more footpath untrod,
One more triumph for devils and sorrow for angels,
    One wrong more to man, one more insult to God!
Life's night begins: let him never come back to us!
    There would be doubt, hesitation and pain,
Forced praise on our part—the glimmer of twilight,
    Never glad confident morning again!

Best fight on well, for we taught him,—strike gallantly,
  Menace our heart ere we master his own;
Then let him receive the new knowledge and wait us,
  Pardoned in Heaven, the first by the throne!

ROBERT BROWNING

THE PATRIOT

IT was roses, roses, all the way,
  With myrtle mixed in my path like mad:
The house-roofs seemed to heave and sway,
  The church-spires flamed, such flags they had,
A year ago on this very day!

The air broke into a mist with bells,
  The old walls rocked with the crowd and cries.
Had I said, 'Good folk, mere noise repels—
  But give me your sun from yonder skies!'
They had answered, 'And afterward, what else?'

Alack, it was I who leaped at the sun
  To give it my loving friends to keep!
Nought man could do, have I left undone:
  And you see my harvest, what I reap
This very day, now a year is run.

There's nobody on the house-tops now—
  Just a palsied few at the windows set;
For the best of the sight is, all allow,
  At the Shambles' Gate—or, better yet,
By the very scaffold's foot, I trow.

I go in the rain, and, more than needs,
 A rope cuts both my wrists behind;
And I think, by the feel, my forehead bleeds,
 For they fling, whoever has a mind,
Stones at me for my year's misdeeds.

Thus I entered, and thus I go!
 In triumphs, people have dropped down dead.
'Paid by the World,—what dost thou owe
 Me?' God might question: now instead,
'Tis God shall repay! I am safer so.

ROBERT BROWNING

THE BURIAL-MARCH OF DUNDEE

John Graeme of Claverhouse, Viscount Dundee, raised a Highland army for the exiled James II in 1689.

SOUND the fife, and cry the slogan—
 Let the pibroch[1] shake the air
With its wild triumphal music,
 Worthy of the freight we bear.
Let the ancient hills of Scotland
 Hear once more the battle-song
Swell within their glens and valleys
 As the clansmen march along!
Never from the field of combat,
 Never from the deadly fray,
Was a nobler trophy carried

[1] gathering-song

Than we bring with us to-day—
Never, since the valiant Douglas
  On his dauntless bosom bore
Good King Robert's heart—the priceless—
  To our dear Redeemer's shore!
Lo! we bring with us the hero—
  Lo! we bring the conquering Graeme,
Crowned as best beseems a victor
  From the altar of his fame;
Fresh and bleeding from the battle
  Whence his spirit took its flight,
Midst the crashing charge of squadrons,
  And the thunder of the fight!
Strike, I say, the notes of triumph,
  As we march o'er moor and lea!
Is there any here will venture
  To bewail our dead Dundee?
Let the widows of the traitors
  Weep until their eyes are dim!
Wail ye may full well for Scotland—
  Let none dare to mourn for him!
See! above his glorious body
  Lies the royal banner's fold—
See! his valiant blood is mingled—
  With its crimson and its gold—
See how calm he looks, and stately,
  Like a warrior on his shield,
Waiting till the flush of morning
  Breaks along the battle-field!
See—Oh never more, my comrades,
  Shall we see that falcon eye

Redden with its inward lightning,
　　As the hour of fight drew nigh!
Never shall we hear the voice that,
　　Clearer than the trumpet's call,
Bade us strike for King and Country,
　　Bade us win the field, or fall!

On the heights of Killiecrankie
　　Yester-morn our army lay:
Slowly rose the mist in columns
　　From the river's broken way;
Hoarsely roared the swollen torrent,
　　And the Pass was wrapt in gloom,
When the clansmen rose together
　　From their lair amidst the broom.
Then we belted on our tartans,
　　And our bonnets down we drew,
And we felt our broadswords' edges,
　　And we proved them to be true;
And we prayed the prayer of soldiers,
　　And we cried the gathering-cry,
And we clasped the hands of kinsmen,
　　And we swore to do or die!
Then our leader rode before us
　　On his war-horse black as night—
Well the Cameronian rebels
　　Knew that charger in the fight!—
And a cry of exultation
　　From the bearded warriors rose;
For we loved the house of Claver'se,

And we thought of good Montrose.
But he raised his hand for silence—
   'Soldiers! I have sworn a vow:
Ere the evening star shall glisten
   On Schehallion's lofty brow,
Either we shall rest in triumph,
   Or another of the Graemes
Shall have died in battle-harness
   For his Country and King James!
Think upon the Royal Martyr—
   Think of what his race endure—
Think of him whom butchers murdered
   On the field of Magus Muir:—
By his sacred blood I charge ye,
   By the ruined hearth and shrine—
By the blighted hopes of Scotland,
   By your injuries and mine—
Strike this day as if the anvil
   Lay beneath your blows the while,
Be they covenanting traitors,
   Or the brood of false Argyle!
Strike! and drive the trembling rebels
   Backwards o'er the stormy Forth;
Let them tell their pale Convention
   How they fared within the North.
Let them tell that Highland honour
   Is not to be bought nor sold,
That we scorn their prince's anger
   As we loathe his foreign gold.
Strike! and when the fight is over,
   If ye look in vain for me,

Where the dead are lying thickest,
 Search for him that was Dundee!'

Loudly then the hills re-echoed
 With our answer to his call,
But a deeper echo sounded
 In the bosoms of us all.
For the lands of wide Breadalbane,
 Not a man who heard him speak
Would that day have left the battle.
 Burning eye and flushing cheek
Told the clansmen's fierce emotion,
 And they harder drew their breath;
For their souls were strong within them,
 Stronger than the grasp of death.
Soon we heard a challenge-trumpet
 Sounding in the Pass below,
And the distant tramp of horses,
 And the voices of the foe:
Down we crouched amid the bracken,
 Till the Lowland ranks drew near,
Panting like the hounds in summer,
 When they scent the stately deer.
From the dark defile emerging,
 Next we saw the squadrons come,
Leslie's foot and Leven's troopers
 Marching to the tuck of drum;
Through the scattered wood of birches,
 O'er the broken ground and heath,
Wound the long battalion slowly,
 Till they gained the plain beneath;

Then we bounded from our covert.—
　Judge how looked the Saxons then,
When they saw the rugged mountain
　Start to life with arméd men!
Like a tempest down the ridges
　Swept the hurricane of steel,
Rose the slogan of Macdonald—
　Flashed the broadsword of Locheill!
Vainly sped the withering volley
　'Mongst the foremost of our band—
On we poured until we met them,
　Foot to foot, and hand to hand.
Horse and man went down like drift-wood
　When the floods are black at Yule,
And their carcasses are whirling
　In the Garry's deepest pool.
Horse and man went down before us—
　Living foe there tarried none
On the field of Killiecrankie,
　When that stubborn fight was done!

And the evening star was shining
　On Schehallion's distant head,
When we wiped our bloody broadswords,
　And returned to count the dead.
There we found him gashed and gory,
　Stretched upon the cumbered plain,
As he told us where to seek him,
　In the thickest of the slain.
And a smile was on his visage,
　For within his dying ear

Pealed the joyful note of triumph,
    And the clansmen's clamorous cheer:
So, amidst the battle's thunder,
    Shot, and steel, and scorching flame,
In the glory of his manhood
    Passed the spirit of the Graeme!

Open wide the vaults of Atholl,
    Where the bones of heroes rest—
Open wide the hallowed portals
    To receive another guest!
Last of Scots, and last of freemen—
    Last of all that dauntless race,
Who would rather die unsullied
    Than outlive the land's disgrace!
O thou lion-hearted warrior!
    Reck not of the after-time:
Honour may be deemed dishonour,
    Loyalty be called a crime.
Sleep in peace with kindred ashes
    Of the noble and the true,
Hands that never failed their country,
    Hearts that never baseness knew.
Sleep!—and till the latest trumpet
    Wakes the dead from earth and sea,
Scotland shall not boast a braver
    Chieftain than our own Dundee!

WILLIAM AYTOUN

SAY NOT THE STRUGGLE NAUGHT AVAILETH

SAY not the struggle naught availeth,
  The labour and the wounds are vain,
The enemy faints not, nor faileth,
  And as things have been things remain.

If hopes were dupes, fears may be liars;
  It may be, in yon smoke conceal'd,
Your comrades chase e'en now the fliers,
  And, but for you, possess the field.

For while the tired waves, vainly breaking,
  Seem here no painful inch to gain,
Far back, through creeks and inlets making,
  Comes silent, flooding in, the main.

And not by eastern windows only,
  When daylight comes, comes in the light;
In front the sun climbs slow, how slowly!
  But westward, look, the land is bright!

ARTHUR HUGH CLOUGH

O CAPTAIN! MY CAPTAIN!

O CAPTAIN! my Captain! our fearful trip is done,
  The ship has weathered every rack, the prize we
    sought is won,
The port is near, the bells I hear, the people all exulting,
While follow eyes the steady keel, the vessel grim and
    daring;
            But O heart! heart! heart!
              O the bleeding drops of red,
                Where on the deck my Captain lies,
                  Fallen cold and dead.

O Captain! my Captain! rise up and hear the bells;
Rise up—for you the flag is flung—for you the bugle
    trills,
For you bouquets and ribboned wreaths—for you the
    shores a-crowding,
For you they call, the swaying mass, their eager faces
    turning;
            Here, Captain! dear father!
              This arm beneath your head!
                It is some dream that on the deck
                  You've fallen cold and dead.

My Captain does not answer, his lips are pale and still,
My father does not feel my arm, he has no pulse nor will;

The ship is anchored safe and sound, its voyage closed
   and done,
From fearful trip the victor ship comes in with object
   won;
   Exult, O shores! and ring, O bells!
      But I, with mournful tread,
         Walk the deck my Captain lies,
            Fallen cold and dead.

WALT WHITMAN

THE LAST WORD

CREEP into thy narrow bed,
   Creep, and let no more be said!
Vain thy onset! all stands fast;
Thou thyself must break at last.

Let the long contention cease!
Geese are swans, and swans are geese.
Let them have it how they will!
Thou art tired; best be still!

They out-talk'd thee, hiss'd thee, tore thee.
Better men fared thus before thee;
Fired their ringing shot and pass'd,
Hotly charged—and broke at last.

Charge once more, then, and be dumb!
Let the victors, when they come,
When the forts of folly fall,
Find thy body by the wall.

MATTHEW ARNOLD

FROM 'SOHRAB AND RUSTUM'

*Sohrab, son of the Persian hero Rustum, has joined the Tartar forces and become
their champion. Rustum and Sohrab engage in single combat, neither knowing the
identity of the other, and Rustum kills his son.*

HE spoke; and Sohrab kindled at his taunts,
And he too drew his sword: at once they rush'd
Together, as two eagles on one prey
Come rushing down together from the clouds,
One from the east, one from the west: their shields
Dash'd with a clang together, and a din
Rose, such as that the sinewy woodcutters
Make often in the forest's heart at morn,
Of hewing axes, crashing trees: such blows
Rustum and Sohrab on each other hail'd.
And you would say that sun and stars took part
In that unnatural conflict; for a cloud
Grew suddenly in Heaven, and dark'd the sun
Over the fighters' heads; and a wind rose
Under their feet, and moaning swept the plain,
And in a sandy whirlwind wrapp'd the pair.
In gloom they twain were wrapp'd, and they alone;
For both the on-looking hosts on either hand
Stood in broad daylight, and the sky was pure,
And the sun sparkled on the Oxus stream.
But in the gloom they fought, with bloodshot eyes
And labouring breath; first Rustum struck the shield
Which Sohrab held stiff out: the steel-spik'd spear
Rent the tough plates, but fail'd to reach the skin,
And Rustum pluck'd it back with angry groan.
Then Sohrab with his sword smote Rustum's helm,
Nor clove its steel quite through; but all the crest

He shore away, and that proud horsehair plume,
Never till now defil'd, sunk to the dust;
And Rustum bow'd his head; but then the gloom
Grew blacker: thunder rumbled in the air,
And lightnings rent the cloud; and Ruksh, the horse,
Who stood at hand, utter'd a dreadful cry:
No horse's cry was that, most like the roar
Of some pain'd desert lion, who all day
Has trail'd the hunter's javelin in his side,
And comes at night to die upon the sand:—
The two hosts heard that cry, and quak'd for fear,
And Oxus curdled as it cross'd his stream.
But Sohrab heard, and quail'd not, but rush'd on,
And struck again; and again Rustum bow'd
His head; but this time all the blade, like glass,
Sprang in a thousand shivers on the helm,
And in his hand the hilt remain'd alone.
Then Rustum rais'd his head: his dreadful eyes
Glar'd, and he shook on high his menacing spear,
And shouted, *Rustum!* Sohrab heard that shout.
And shrank amaz'd: back he recoil'd one step,
And scann'd with blinking eyes the advancing Form:
And then he stood bewilder'd; and he dropp'd
His covering shield, and the spear pierc'd his side,
He reel'd, and staggering back, sunk to the ground.
And then the gloom dispers'd, and the wind fell,
And the bright sun broke forth, and melted all
The cloud; and the two armies saw the pair;
Saw Rustum standing, safe upon his feet,
And Sohrab, wounded, on the bloody sand.

MATTHEW ARNOLD

FROM 'BALDER DEAD'

(*The Funeral*)

But when the Gods and Heroes heard, they brought
The wood to Balder's ship, and built a pile,
Full the deck's breadth, and lofty; then the corpse
Of Balder on the highest top they laid,
With Nanna on his right, and on his left
Hoder, his brother, whom his own hand slew.
And they set jars of wine and oil to lean
Against the bodies, and stuck torches near,
Splinters of pine-wood, soak'd with turpentine;
And brought his arms and gold, and all his stuff,
And slew the dogs which at his table fed,
And his horse, Balder's horse, whom most he lov'd,
And threw them on the pyre, and Odin threw
A last choice gift thereon, his golden ring.
They fixt the mast, and hoisted up the sails,
Then they put fire to the wood; and Thor
Set his stout shoulder hard against the stern
To push the ship through the thick sand: sparks flew
From the deep trench she plough'd—so strong a God
Furrow'd it—and the water gurgled in.
And the Ship floated on the waves, and rock'd:
But in the hills a strong East-Wind arose,
And came down moaning to the sea; first squalls
Ran black o'er the sea's face, then steady rush'd
The breeze, and fill'd the sails, and blew the fire.
And, wreath'd in smoke, the Ship stood out to sea.
Soon with a roaring rose the mighty fire,

And the pile crackled; and between the logs
Sharp quivering tongues of flame shot out, and leapt,
Curling and darting, higher, until they lick'd
The summit of the pile, the dead, the mast,
And ate the shrivelling sails; but still the Ship
Drove on, ablaze, above her hull, with fire.
And the Gods stood upon the beach, and gaz'd:
And, while they gaz'd, the Sun went lurid down
Into the smoke-wrapt sea, and Night came on.
Then the wind fell, with night, and there was calm.
But through the dark they watch'd the burning Ship
Still carried o'er the distant waters on
Farther and farther, like an Eye of Fire.
And as in the dark night a travelling man
Who bivouacs in a forest 'mid the hills,
Sees suddenly a spire of flame shoot up
Out of the black waste forest, far below,
Which woodcutters have lighted near their lodge
Against the wolves; and all night long it flares:—
So flar'd, in the far darkness, Balder's pyre.
But fainter, as the stars rose high, it burn'd;
The bodies were consum'd, ash chok'd the pile:
And as in a decaying winter fire
A charr'd log, falling, makes a shower of sparks—
So, with a shower of sparks, the pile fell in,
Reddening the sea around; and all was dark.

MATTHEW ARNOLD

REQUIESCAT

STREW on her roses, roses,
 And never a spray of yew.
In quiet she reposes:
  Ah! would that I did too.

Her mirth the world required:
  She bath'd it in smiles of glee.
But her heart was tired, tired,
  And now they let her be.

Her life was turning, turning,
  In mazes of heat and sound.
But for peace her soul was yearning
  And now peace laps her round.

Her cabin'd, ample Spirit,
  It flutter'd and fail'd for breath.
To-night it doth inherit
  The vasty hall of Death.

MATTHEW ARNOLD

HERACLITUS

Εἶπέ τις, Ἡράκλειτε, τεὸν μόρον

THEY told me, Heraclitus, they told me you were
 dead;
They brought me bitter news to hear and bitter tears
  to shed.

I wept as I remembered how often you and I
Had tired the sun with talking and sent him down the
   sky.

And now that thou art lying, my dear old Carian guest,
A handful of grey ashes, long long ago at rest,
Still are thy pleasant voices, thy nightingales, awake,
For Death, he taketh all away, but them he cannot take.

WILLIAM CORY (WILLIAM JOHNSON)

WHEN I AM DEAD, MY DEAREST

WHEN I am dead, my dearest,
   Sing no sad songs for me;
Plant thou no roses at my head,
   Nor shady cypress-tree:
Be the green grass above me
   With showers and dewdrops wet:
And if thou wilt, remember,
   And if thou wilt, forget.

I shall not see the shadows,
   I shall not feel the rain;
I shall not hear the nightingale
   Sing on, as if in pain:
And dreaming through the twilight
   That doth not rise nor set,
Haply I may remember,
   And haply may forget.

CHRISTINA ROSSETTI

A BALLAD TO QUEEN ELIZABETH
of the Spanish Armada

King Philip had vaunted his claims;
    He had sworn for a year he would sack us;
With an army of heathenish names
    He was coming to fagot and stack us;
    Like the thieves of the sea he would track us,
And shatter our ships on the main;
    But we had bold Neptune to back us—
And where are the galleons of Spain?

His carackes[1] were christened of dames
    To the kirtles[2] whereof he would tack us;
With his saints and his gilded stern-frames
    He had thought like an egg-shell to crack us;
    Now Howard may get to his Flaccus,
And Drake to his Devon again,
    And Hawkins bowl rubbers to Bacchus—
For where are the galleons of Spain?

Let his Majesty hang to St. James
    The axe that he whetted to hack us;
He must play at some lustier games
    Or at sea he can hope to out-thwack us;
    To his mines of Peru he would pack us
To tug at his bullet and chain;
    Alas! that his Greatness should lack us!—
But where are the galleons of Spain?

[1] galleons   [2] petticoats

GLORIANA![1]—the Don may attack us
Whenever his stomach be fain;
  He must reach us before he can rack us,
And where are the galleons of Spain?

AUSTIN DOBSON

LONDON SNOW

WHEN men were all asleep the snow came flying,
  In large white flakes falling on the city brown,
Stealthily and perpetually settling and loosely lying,
  Hushing the latest traffic of the drowsy town;
Deadening, muffling, stifling its murmurs failing;
Lazily and incessantly floating down and down:
  Silently sifting and veiling road, roof and railing;
Hiding difference, making unevenness even,
Into angles and crevices softly drifting and sailing.
  All night it fell, and when full inches seven
It lay in the depth of its uncompacted lightness,
The clouds blew off from a high and frosty heaven;
  And all woke earlier for the unaccustomed brightness
Of the winter dawning, the strange unheavenly glare:
The eye marvelled—marvelled at the dazzling white-
    ness;
  The ear hearkened to the stillness of the solemn air;
No sound of wheel rumbling nor of foot falling,
And the busy morning cries came thin and spare.

[1] Queen Elizabeth

Then boys I heard, as they went to school, calling,
They gathered up the crystal manna to freeze
Their tongues with tasting, their hands with snow-
    balling;
Or rioted in a drift, plunging up to the knees;
Or peering up from under the white-mossed wonder,
'O look at the trees!' they cried, 'O look at the trees!'

With lessened load a few carts creak and blunder,
Following along the white deserted way,
A country company long dispersed asunder:
When now already the sun, in pale display
Standing by Paul's high dome, spread forth below
His sparkling beams, and awoke the stir of the day.

For now doors open, and war is waged with the snow;
And trains of sombre men, past tale of number,
Tread long brown paths, as toward their toil they go:
But even for them awhile no cares encumber
Their minds diverted; the daily word is unspoken,
The daily thoughts of labour and sorrow slumber
At the sight of the beauty that greets them, for the
    charm they have broken.

ROBERT BRIDGES

A PASSER-BY

WHITHER, O splendid ship, thy white sails crowding,
    Leaning across the bosom of the urgent West,
That fearest nor sea rising, nor sky clouding,
    Whither away, fair rover, and what thy quest?
    Ah! soon, when Winter has all our vales opprest,
When skies are cold and misty, and hail is hurling,
    Wilt thóu glíde on the blue Pacific, or rest
In a summer haven asleep, thy white sails furling.

I there before thee, in the country that well thou
        knowest,
    Already arrived am inhaling the odorous air:
I watch thee enter unerringly where thou goest,
    And anchor queen of the strange shipping there,
    Thy sails for awnings spread, thy masts bare:
Nor is aught from the foaming reef to the snow-capped,
        grandest
    Peak, that is over the feathery palms, more fair
Than thou, so upright, so stately, and still thou standest.

And yet, O splendid ship, unhailed and nameless,
    I know not if, aiming a fancy, I rightly divine
That thou hast a purpose joyful, a courage blameless,
    Thy port assured in a happier land than mine.
    But for all I have given thee, beauty enough is thine,
As thou, aslant with trim tackle and shrouding,
    From the proud nostril curve of a prow's line
In the offing scatterest foam, thy white sails crowding.

ROBERT BRIDGES

FIRST SPRING MORNING

Look! Look! the spring is come:
    O feel the gentle air,
That wanders thro' the boughs to burst
    The thick buds everywhere!
    The birds are glad to see
    The high unclouded sun:
Winter is fled away, they sing,
    The gay time is begun.

Adown the meadows green
    Let us go dance and play,
And look for violets in the lane,
    And ramble far away
    To gather primroses,
    That in the woodland grow,
And hunt for oxlips, or if yet
    The blades of bluebells show:

There the old woodman gruff
    Hath half the coppice cut,
And weaves the hurdles all day long
    Beside his willow hut.
    We'll steal on him, and then
    Startle him, all with glee
Singing our song of winter fled
    And summer soon to be.

ROBERT BRIDGES

THE VAGABOND

Give to me the life I love,
  Let the lave[1] go by me,
Give the jolly heaven above
  And the by-way nigh me.
Bed in the bush with stars to see,
  Bread I dip in the river—
There's the life for a man like me,
  There's the life for ever.

Let the blow fall soon or late,
  Let what will be o'er me;
Give the face of earth around
  And the road before me.
Wealth I seek not, hope nor love,
  Nor a friend to know me;
All I seek, the heaven above,
  And the road below me.

Or let autumn fall on me
  Where afield I linger,
Silencing the bird on tree,
  Biting the blue finger.
White as meal the frosty field—
  Warm the fireside haven—
Not to autumn will I yield,
  Not to winter even!

[1] rest

Let the blow fall soon or late,
    Let what will be o'er me;
Give the face of earth around,
    And the road before me.
Wealth I ask not, hope nor love,
    Nor a friend to know me.
All I ask, the heaven above,
    And the road below me.

ROBERT LOUIS STEVENSON

RECESSIONAL

GOD of our fathers, known of old,
    Lord of our far-flung battle-line,
Beneath whose awful Hand we hold
    Dominion over palm and pine—
Lord God of Hosts, be with us yet,
Lest we forget—lest we forget!

The tumult and the shouting dies;
    The captains and the kings depart:
Still stands Thine ancient sacrifice,
    An humble and a contrite heart.
Lord God of Hosts, be with us yet,
Lest we forget—lest we forget!

Far-called, our navies melt away.
    On dune and headland sinks the fire:
Lo, all our pomp of yesterday
    Is one with Nineveh and Tyre!
Judge of the Nations, spare us yet,
Lest we forget—lest we forget!

If, drunk with sight of power, we loose
    Wild tongues that have not Thee in awe,
Such boastings as the Gentiles use,
    Or lesser breeds without the Law—
Lord God of Hosts, be with us yet,
Lest we forget—lest we forget!

For heathen heart that puts her trust
    In reeking tube and iron shard,
All valiant dust that builds on dust,
    And guarding, calls not Thee to guard,
For frantic boast and foolish word—
Thy Mercy on Thy People, Lord!

                 RUDYARD KIPLING

THE WAY THROUGH THE WOODS

THEY shut the road through the woods
    Seventy years ago.
Weather and rain have undone it again,
    And now you would never know
There was once a road through the woods
    Before they planted the trees.
It is underneath the coppice and heath,
    And the thin anemones.
    Only the keeper sees
That, where the ring-dove broods,
    And the badgers roll at ease,
There was once a road through the woods.

Yet, if you enter the woods
    Of a summer evening late,
When the night-air cools on the trout-ringed pools
    Where the otter whistles his mate
(They fear not men in the woods,
    Because they see so few)
You will hear the beat of a horse's feet
    And the swish of a skirt in the dew,
    Steadily cantering through
The misty solitudes,
    As though they perfectly knew
The old lost road through the woods. . . .
But there is no road through the woods.

                    RUDYARD KIPLING

THE LAKE ISLE OF INNISFREE

I WILL arise and go now, and go to Innisfree,
And a small cabin build there, of clay and wattles
made;
Nine bean rows will I have there, a hive for the honey
bee,
And live alone in the bee-loud glade.

And I shall have some peace there, for peace comes
dropping slow,
Dropping from the veils of the morning to where the
cricket sings;
There midnight's all a glimmer, and noon a purple
glow,
And evening full of the linnet's wings.

I will arise and go now, for always night and day
I hear lake water lapping with low sounds by the shore;
While I stand on the roadway, or on the pavements
grey,
I hear it in the deep heart's core.

WILLIAM BUTLER YEATS

THE SONG OF WANDERING AENGUS

I WENT out to the hazel wood,
Because a fire was in my head,
And cut and peeled a hazel wand,
And hooked a berry to a thread;
And when white moths were on the wing,
And moth-like stars were flickering out,
I dropped the berry in a stream
And caught a little silver trout.

When I had laid it on the floor
I went to blow the fire a-flame,
But something rustled on the floor,
And some one called me by my name:
It had become a glimmering girl
With apple blossom in her hair
Who called me by my name and ran
And faded through the brightening air.

Though I am old with wandering
Through hollow lands and hilly lands,
I will find out where she has gone,
And kiss her lips and take her hands;
And walk among long dappled grass,
And pluck till time and times are done
The silver apples of the moon,
The golden apples of the sun.

WILLIAM BUTLER YEATS

AN IRISH AIRMAN FORESEES HIS DEATH

I KNOW that I shall meet my fate
Somewhere among the clouds above;
Those that I fight I do not hate,
Those that I guard I do not love;
My country is Kiltartan Cross,
My countrymen Kiltartan's poor,
No likely end could bring them loss
Or leave them happier than before.
Nor law, nor duty bade me fight,
Nor public men, nor cheering crowds,
A lonely impulse of delight
Drove to this tumult in the clouds;
I balanced all, brought all to mind,
The years to come seemed waste of breath,
A waste of breath the years behind
In balance with this life, this death.

WILLIAM BUTLER YEATS

FOR THE FALLEN

WITH proud thanksgiving, a mother for her chil-
dren,
England mourns for her dead across the sea.
Flesh of her flesh they were, spirit of her spirit,
Fallen in the cause of the free.

Solemn the drums thrill: Death august and royal
Sings sorrow up into immortal spheres.
There is music in the midst of desolation
And a glory that shines upon our tears.

They went with songs to the battle, they were young,
Straight of limb, true of eye, steady and aglow.
They were staunch to the end against odds uncounted,
They fell with their faces to the foe.

They shall grow not old, as we that are left grow old:
Age shall not weary them, nor the years condemn.
At the going down of the sun and in the morning
We will remember them.

They mingle not with their laughing comrades again;
They sit no more at familiar tables of home;
They have no lot in our labour of the day-time:
They sleep beyond England's foam.

But where our desires are and our hopes profound,
Felt as a well-spring that is hidden from sight,
To the innermost heart of their own land they are
    known
As the stars are known to the Night;

As the stars that shall be bright when we are dust,
Moving in marches upon the heavenly plain,
As the stars that are starry in the time of our darkness,
To the end, to the end, they remain.

LAURENCE BINYON

THE BELLS OF HEAVEN

'TWOULD ring the bells of Heaven
   The wildest peal for years,
If Parson lost his senses
And people came to theirs,
And he and they together
Knelt down with angry prayers
For tamed and shabby tigers
And dancing dogs and bears,
And wretched, blind pit ponies,
And little hunted hares.

RALPH HODGSON

THE LISTENERS

'IS there anybody there?' said the Traveller,
   Knocking on the moonlit door;
And his horse in the silence champed the grasses
   Of the forest's ferny floor:
And a bird flew up out of the turret,
   Above the Traveller's head:
And he smote upon the door again a second time;
   'Is there anybody there?' he said.
But no one descended to the Traveller;
   No head from the leaf-fringed sill
Leaned over and looked into his grey eyes,
   Where he stood perplexed and still.
But only a host of phantom listeners
   That dwelt in the lone house then

Stood listening in the quiet of the moonlight
To that voice from the world of men:
Stood thronging the faint moonbeams on the dark stair,
That goes down to the empty hall,
Hearkening in an air stirred and shaken
By the lonely Traveller's call.
And he felt in his heart their strangeness,
Their stillness answering his cry,
While his horse moved, cropping the dark turf,
'Neath the starred and leafy sky;
For he suddenly smote on the door, even
Louder, and lifted his head:—
'Tell them I came, and no one answered,
That I kept my word,' he said.
Never the least stir made the listeners,
Though every word he spake
Fell echoing through the shadowiness of the still house
From the one man left awake:
Ay, they heard his foot upon the stirrup,
And the sound of iron on stone,
And how the silence surged softly backward,
When the plunging hoofs were gone.

WALTER DE LA MARE

SILVER

SLOWLY, silently, now the moon
   Walks the night in her silver shoon;
This way, and that, she peers, and sees
Silver fruit upon silver trees;
One by one the casements catch
Her beams beneath the silvery thatch;
Couched in his kennel, like a log,
With paws of silver sleeps the dog;
From their shadowy cote the white breasts **peep**
Of doves in a silver-feathered sleep;
A harvest mouse goes scampering by,
With silver claws, and silver eye;
And moveless fish in the water gleam,
By silver reeds in a silver stream.

WALTER DE LA MARE

THE DONKEY

WHEN fishes flew and forests walked
   And figs grew upon thorn,
Some moment when the moon was blood
   Then surely I was born;

With monstrous head and sickening cry
   And ears like errant wings,
The devil's walking parody
   On all four-footed things.

The tattered outlaw of the earth,
    Of ancient crooked will;
Starve, scourge, deride me: I am dumb,
    I keep my secret still.

Fools! For I also had my hour;
    One far fierce hour and sweet:
There was a shout about my ears,
    And palms before my feet.

G. K. CHESTERTON

FROM 'LEPANTO'

*Don John of Austria, half-brother of Philip II of Spain, com-
manded a large fleet of Spanish and Italian galleys against the
Turks, and won the decisive battle of Lepanto in 1571, which
saved Christendom from the Turkish menace.*

WHITE founts falling in the courts of the sun,
    And the Soldan of Byzantium is smiling as they
    run;
There is laughter like the fountains in that face of all
    men feared,
It stirs the forest darkness, the darkness of his beard,
It curls the blood-red crescent, the crescent of his lips,
For the inmost sea of all the earth is shaken with his
    ships.
They have dared the white republics up the capes of
    Italy,   [Sea,
They have dashed the Adriatic round the Lion of the

And the Pope has cast his arms abroad for agony and
    loss,
And called the kings of Christendom for swords about
    the Cross,
The cold queen of England is looking in the glass;
The shadow of the Valois is yawning at the Mass;
From evening isles fantastical rings faint the Spanish
    gun,
And the Lord upon the Golden Horn is laughing in the
    sun.

Dim drums throbbing, in the hills half heard,
Where only on a nameless throne a crownless prince has
    stirred,
Where, risen from a doubtful seat and half attainted
    stall,
The last knight of Europe takes weapons from the wall,
The last and lingering troubadour to whom the bird has
    sung,
That once went singing southward when all the world
    was young,
In that enormous silence, tiny and unafraid,
Comes up along a winding road the noise of the Crusade.
Strong gongs groaning as the guns boom far,
Don John of Austria is going to the war,
Stiff flags straining in the night-blasts cold
In the gloom black-purple, in the glint old-gold,
Torchlight crimson on the copper kettle-drums,
Then the tuckets, then the trumpets, then the cannon,
    and he comes.

Don John laughing in the brave beard curled,
Spurning of his stirrups like the thrones of all the world,
Holding his head up for a flag of all the free.
Love-light of Spain—hurrah!
Death-light of Africa!
Don John of Austria!
Is riding to the sea.

. . . .

The Pope was in his chapel before day or battle broke,
(*Don John of Austria is hidden in the smoke.*)   [year,
The hidden room in a man's house where God sits all the
The secret window whence the world looks small and
          very dear.
He sees as in a mirror on the monstrous twilight sea
The crescent of his cruel ships whose name is mystery;
They fling great shadows foe-wards, making Cross and
          Castle dark,
They veil the pluméd lions on the galleys of St. Mark;
And above the ships are palaces of brown, black-
          bearded chiefs,
And below the ships are prisons, where with multitudi-
          nous griefs,
Christian captives sick and sunless, all a labouring race
          repines
Like a race in sunken cities, like a nation in the mines.
They are lost like slaves that swat, and in the skies of
          morning hung   [young.
The stairways of the tallest gods when tyranny was
They are countless, voiceless, hopeless as those fallen or
          fleeing on
Before the high Kings' horses in the granite of Babylon.

And many a one grows witless in his quiet room in hell,
Where a yellow face looks inward through the lattice of
    his cell,
And he finds his God forgotten, and he seeks no more a
    sign—
    (*But Don John of Austria has burst the battle line!*)
Don John pounding from the slaughter-painted poop,
Purpling all the ocean like a bloody pirate's sloop,
Scarlet running over on the silvers and the golds,
Breaking of the hatches up and bursting of the holds,
Thronging of the thousands up that labour under sea
White for bliss and blind for sun and stunned for liberty.
Vivat Hispania!
Domino Gloria!
Don John of Austria
Has set his people free!

   .   .   .   .

                           G. K. CHESTERTON

SPANISH WATERS

SPANISH waters, Spanish waters, you are ringing in
my ears,
Like a slow sweet piece of music from the grey forgotten
years;
Telling tales, and beating tunes, and bringing weary
thoughts to me
Of the sandy beach at Muertos, where I would that I
could be.

There's a surf breaks on Los Muertos, and it never
stops to roar,
And it's there we came to anchor, and it's there we
went ashore,
Where the blue lagoon is silent amid snags of rotting
trees,
Dropping like the clothes of corpses cast up by the seas.

We anchored at Los Muertos when the dipping sun was
red,
We left her half-a-mile to sea, to west of Nigger Head;
And before the mist was on the Cay, before the day was
done,
We were all ashore on Muertos with the gold that we
had won.

We bore it through the marshes in a half-score battered
chests,
Sinking in the sucking quagmires to the sunburn on our
breasts,

Heaving over tree-trunks, gasping, damning at the flies
    and heat,
Longing for a long drink, out of silver, in the ship's cool
    lazareet.[1]

The moon came white and ghostly as we laid the
    treasure down,
There was gear there'd make a beggarman as rich as
    Lima Town,
Copper charms and silver trinkets from the chests of
    Spanish crews,
Gold doubloons and double moidores, louis d'ors and
    portagues,[2]

Clumsy yellow-metal earrings from the Indians of Brazil,
Uncut emeralds out of Rio, bezoar stones from Guaya-
    quil;
Silver, in the crude and fashioned, pots of old Aríca
    bronze,
Jewels from the bones of Incas desecrated by the Dons.

We smoothed the place with mattocks, and we took and
    blazed the tree,
Which marks you where the gear is hid that none will
    ever see,
And we laid aboard the ship again, and south away we
    steers,
Through the loud surf of Los Muertos which is beating
    in my ears.

[1] store-room   [2] Portuguese gold coins

I'm the last alive that knows it. All the rest have gone
    their ways
Killed, or died, or come to anchor in the old Mulatas
    Cays,
And I go singing, fiddling, old and starved and in des-
    pair,
And I know where all that gold is hid, if I were only
    there.

It's not the way to end it all. I'm old, and nearly blind,
And an old man's past's a strange thing, for it never
    leaves his mind.
And I see in dreams, awhiles, the beach, the sun's disc
    dipping red,
And the tall ship, under topsails, swaying in past Nigger
    Head.

I'd be glad to step ashore there. Glad to take a pick and
    go
To the lone blazed coco-palm tree in the place no others
    know,
And lift the gold and silver that has mouldered there
    for years
By the loud surf of Los Muertos which is beating in my
    ears.

JOHN MASEFIELD

LAUGH AND BE MERRY

LAUGH and be merry, remember, better the world
with a song,
Better the world with a blow in the teeth of a wrong.
Laugh, for the time is brief, a thread the length of a
span.
Laugh and be proud to belong to the old proud pageant
of man.

Laugh and be merry: remember, in olden time,
God made Heaven and Earth for joy He took in a rhyme,
Made them, and filled them full with the strong red
wine of His mirth,
The splendid joy of the stars: the joy of the earth.

So we must laugh and drink from the deep blue cup of
the sky
Join the jubilant song of the great stars sweeping by,
Laugh, and battle, and work, and drink of the wine
outpoured
In the dear green earth, the sign of the joy of the Lord.

Laugh and be merry together, like brothers akin,
Guesting awhile in the rooms of a beautiful inn,
Glad till the dancing stops, and the lilt of the music ends.
Laugh till the game is played; and be you merry, my
friends.

JOHN MASEFIELD

THE RIDER AT THE GATE

A WINDY night was blowing on Rome,
  The cressets guttered on Caesar's home,
The fish-boats, moored at the bridge, were breaking
The rush of the river to yellow foam.

The hinges whined to the shutters shaking,
When clip-clop-clep came a horse-hoof raking
The stones of the road at Caesar's gate;
The spear-butts jarred at the guard's awaking.

'Who goes there?' said the guard at the gate.
'What is the news, that you ride so late?'
'News most pressing, that must be spoken
To Caesar alone, and that cannot wait.'

'The Caesar sleeps; you must show a token
That the news suffice that he be awoken.
What is the news, and whence do you come?
For no light cause may his sleep be broken.'

'Out of the dark of the sands I come,
From the dark of death, with news for Rome.
A word so fell that it must be uttered
Though it strike the soul of the Caesar dumb.'

Caesar turned in his bed and muttered,
With a struggle for breath the lamp-flame guttered;
Calpurnia heard her husband moan:
          'The house is falling,
The beaten men come into their own.'

'Speak your word,' said the guard at the gate;
'Yes, but bear it to Caesar straight,
Say, "Your murderer's knives are honing,
Your killer's gang is lying in wait."

'Out of the wind that is blowing and moaning,
Through the city palace and the country loaning,[1]
I cry, "For the world's sake, Caesar, beware,
And take this warning as my atoning.

' "Beware of the Court, of the palace stair,
Of the downcast friend who speaks so fair,
Keep from the Senate, for Death is going
On many men's feet to meet you there."

'I, who am dead, have ways of knowing
Of the crop of death that the quick are sowing.
I, who was Pompey, cry it aloud
From the dark of death, from the wind blowing.

'I, who was Pompey, once was proud,
Now I lie in the sand without a shroud;
I cry to Caesar out of my pain,
"Caesar, beware, your death is vowed." '

[1] field, common

– 368 –

The light grew grey on the window-pane,
The windcocks swung in a burst of rain,
The window of Caesar flung unshuttered,
The horse-hoofs died into wind again.

Caesar turned in his bed and muttered,
With a struggle for breath the lamp-flame guttered;
Calpurnia heard her husband moan:
     '*The house is falling,*
  The beaten men come into their own.'

JOHN MASEFIELD

THE SOLDIER

IF I should die, think only this of me:
  That there's some corner of a foreign field
That is for ever England. There shall be
  In that rich earth a richer dust concealed;
A dust whom England bore, shaped, made aware,
  Gave, once, her flowers to love, her ways to roam,
A body of England's, breathing English air,
  Washed by the rivers, blest by suns of home.

And think, this heart, all evil shed away,
  A pulse in the eternal mind, no less
    Gives somewhere back the thoughts by England
      given;
Her sights and sounds; dreams happy as her day;
  And laughter, learnt of friends; and gentleness,
    In hearts at peace, under an English heaven.

RUPERT BROOKE

THE DYING PATRIOT

DAY breaks on England down the Kentish hills,
Singing in the silence of the meadow-footing rills,
Day of my dreams, O day!
    I saw them march from Dover, long ago,
    With a silver cross before them, singing low,
Monks of Rome from their home where the blue seas
      break in foam,
    Augustine with his feet of snow.

Noon strikes on England, noon on Oxford town,
—Beauty she was statue cold—there's blood upon her
    gown:
Noon of my dreams, O noon!
    Proud and godly kings had built her, long ago,
    With her towers and tombs and statues all arow,
With her fair and floral air and the love that lingers
      there,
    And the streets where the great men go.

Evening on the olden, the golden sea of Wales,
When the first star shivers and the last wave pales:
O evening dreams!
    There's a house that Britons walked in, long ago,
    Where now the springs of ocean fall and flow,
And the dead robed in red and sea-lilies overhead
    Sway when the long winds blow.

Sleep not, my country: though night is here, afar
Your children of the morning are clamorous for war:
Fire in the night, O dreams!
    Though she send you as she sent you, long ago,
    South to desert, east to ocean, west to snow,
West of these out to seas colder than the Hebrides I must
    go
    Where the fleet of stars is anchored and the young
    Star-captains glow.

JAMES ELROY FLECKER

THE OLD SHIPS

I HAVE seen old ships sail like swans asleep
  Beyond the village which men still call Tyre,
With leaden age o'ercargoed, dipping deep
For Famagusta and the hidden sun
That rings black Cyprus with a lake of fire;
And all those ships were certainly so old,
Who knows how oft with squat and noisy gun,
Questing brown slaves or Syrian oranges,
The pirate Genoese
Hell-raked them till they rolled
Blood, water, fruit and corpses up the hold.
But now through friendly seas they softly run,
Painted the mid-sea blue or shore-sea green,
Still patterned with the vine and grapes in gold.

But I have seen,
Pointing her shapely shadows from the dawn
An image tumbled on a rose-swept bay,

A drowsy ship of some yet older day;
And, wonder's breath indrawn,
Thought I—who knows—who knows—but in that same
(Fished up beyond Ææa, patched up new
—Stern painted brighter blue—)
That talkative, bald-headed seaman came
(Twelve patient comrades sweating at the oar)
From Troy's doom-crimson shore,
And with great lies about his wooden horse
Set the crew laughing, and forgot his course.

It was so old a ship—who knows, who knows?
—And yet so beautiful, I watched in vain
To see the mast burst open with a rose,
And the whole deck put on its leaves again.

JAMES ELROY FLECKER

WAR SONG OF THE SARACENS

WE are they who come faster than fate: we are they
who ride early or late:
We storm at your ivory gate: Pale Kings of the Sunset,
beware!
Not on silk nor in samet we lie, not in curtained
solemnity die
Among women who chatter and cry, and children who
mumble a prayer.
But we sleep by the ropes of the camp, and we rise with
a shout, and we tramp
With the sun or the moon for a lamp, and the spray of
the wind in our hair.

From the lands, where the elephants are, to the forts of
    Merou and Balghar,
Our steel we have brought and our star to shine on the
    ruins of Rûm.
We have marched from the Indus to Spain, and by God
    we will go there again;
We have stood on the shore of the plain where the
    Waters of Destiny boom.
A mart of destruction we made at Jalula where men
    were afraid,
For death was a difficult trade, and the sword was a
    broker of doom;

And the Spear was a Desert Physician who cured not
    a few of ambition,
And drave not a few to perdition with medicine bitter
    and strong:
And the shield was a grief to the fool and as bright as
    a desolate pool,
And as straight as the rock of Stamboul when their
    cavalry thundered along:
For the coward was drowned with the brave when our
    battle sheered up like a wave,
And the dead to the desert we gave, and the glory to
    God in our song.

JAMES ELROY FLECKER

INTO BATTLE

THE naked earth is warm with Spring,
    And with green grass and bursting trees
Leans to the sun's gaze glorying,
    And quivers in the sunny breeze;
And Life is Colour and Warmth and Light,
    And a striving evermore for these;
And he is dead who will not fight;
    And who dies fighting has increase.

The fighting man shall from the sun
    Take warmth, and life from the glowing earth;
Speed with the light-foot winds to run,
    And with the trees to newer birth;
And find, when fighting shall be done,
    Great rest, and fullness after dearth.

All the bright company of Heaven
    Hold him in their high comradeship,
The Dog-Star and the Sisters Seven,
    Orion's Belt and sworded hip.

The woodland trees that stand together,
    They stand to him each one a friend,
They gently speak in the windy weather;
    They guide to valley and ridges' end.

The kestrel hovering by day,
    And the little owls that call by night,
Bid him be swift and keen as they,
    As keen of ear, as swift of sight.

The blackbird sings to him, 'Brother, brother,
    If this be the last song you shall sing
Sing well, for you may not sing another;
    Brother, sing.'

In dreary, doubtful, waiting hours,
    Before the brazen frenzy starts,
The horses show him nobler powers;
    O patient eyes, courageous hearts!

And when the burning moment breaks,
    And all things else are out of mind,
And only Joy of Battle takes
    Him by the throat, and makes him blind—

Through joy and blindness he shall know,
    Not caring much to know, that still,
Nor lead nor steel shall reach him, so
    That it be not the Destined Will.

The thundering line of battle stands,
    And in the air Death moans and sings;
But Day shall clasp him with strong hands,
    And Night shall fold him in soft wings.

JULIAN HENRY GRENFELL

CAPE HORN

THE foghorns echo on the gliding rain,
   The cold sea sleeps, the sails droop, and the sun
Glimmers stone-cold; as though the storms in vain
Had died and left their weary work undone:
And miserable, lone,
The hidden land breathes and is lost again.
Chill from the creaking spars the vapour drips,
Stiff hang the ropes; and through the dimness move
The slow, wet, melancholy-bleating ships,
Mourning the days of tempest when they strove.
Not theirs is now the victor's grim delight,
Not now the triumph over wind and sea;
Sadly they creep amidst the creeping white,
Sadly they wander, drifting helplessly;
And round the savage Horn
Groping, afraid, on windless tides are borne.
And in the silence suddenly puffs the whale;
Swift round and round the scared Cape Pigeons fly:
The lurking winter has forgot the gale,
But under the sad sky
A pallid terror broods, and haunts the shaking sail.

GILES DIXEY

THE SONG OF THE UNGIRT RUNNERS

WE swing ungirded hips,
  And lightened are our eyes,
The rain is on our lips,
We do not run for prize.
We know not whom we trust
Nor whitherward we fare,
But we run because we must
  Through the great wide air.

The waters of the seas
Are troubled as by storm.
The tempest strips the trees
And does not leave them warm.
Does the tearing tempest pause?
Do the tree-tops ask it why?
So we run without a cause
  'Neath the big bare sky.

The rain is on our lips,
We do not run for prize.
But the storm the water whips
And the wave howls to the skies.
The winds arise and strike it
And scatter it like sand,
And we run because we like it
  Through the broad bright land.

CHARLES HAMILTON SORLEY

PART II

FROM 'DOCTOR FAUSTUS'

*Faustus has sold his soul to the Devil, and Mephistophiles, Satan's
messenger, is coming to claim him at midnight. Faustus is here
speaking to himself.*

AH, Faustus,
    Now hast thou but one bare hour to live,
And then thou must be damn'd perpetually!
Stand still, you ever-moving spheres of heaven,
That time may cease, and midnight never come;
Fair Nature's eye, rise, rise again, and make
Perpetual day; or let this hour be but
A year, a month, a week, a natural day,
That Faustus may repent and save his soul!
O lente, lente currite, noctis equi!
The stars move still, time runs, the clock will strike,
The devil will come, and Faustus must be damn'd.
O, I'll leap up to my God!—Who pulls me down?
See, see, where Christ's blood streams in the firmament!
One drop would save my soul, half a drop: ah, my
    Christ!—
Ah, rend not my heart for naming of my Christ!
Yet will I call on him: O, spare me, Lucifer!—
Where is it now? 'tis gone: and see, where God
Stretcheth out his arm, and bends his ireful brows!
Mountains and hills, come, come, and fall on me,
And hide me from the heavy wrath of God!
No, no!
Then will I headlong run into the earth:
Earth, gape! O, no, it will not harbour me!
You stars that reign'd at my nativity,

Whose influence hath allotted death and hell,
Now draw up Faustus, like a foggy mist,
Into the entrails of yon labouring clouds,
That, when you vomit forth into the air,
My limbs may issue from your smoky mouths,
So that my soul may but ascend to heaven!
                              [*The clock strikes the half-hour.*
Ah, half the hour is past! 'twill all be past anon.
O God,
If thou wilt not have mercy on my soul,
Yet for Christ's sake, whose blood hath ransom'd me,
Impose some end to my incessant pain;
Let Faustus live in hell a thousand years,
A hundred thousand, and at last be sav'd!
O, no end is limited to damnéd souls!
Why wert thou not a creature wanting soul?
Or why is this immortal that thou hast?
Ah, Pythagóras' metempsýchosis,
Were that true, this soul should fly from me,
And I be chang'd unto some brutish beast!
All beasts are happy, for, when they die,
Their souls are soon dissolv'd in elements;
But mine must live still to be plagu'd in hell.
Curs'd be the parents that engender'd me!
No, Faustus, curse thyself, curse Lucifer
That hath depriv'd thee of the joys of heaven
                              [*The clock strikes twelve.*
O, it strikes, it strikes!   Now, body, turn to air,
Or Lucifer will bear thee quick to hell!
                              [*Thunder and lightning.*
O soul, be changed into little water-drops,

And fall into the ocean, ne'er be found!
My God, my God, look not so fierce on me!

[Enter devils.

Adders and serpents, let me breathe awhile:
Ugly Hell gape not, come not Lucifer,
I'll burn my books, ah! Mephistophiles!

[Exeunt with him.

CHRISTOPHER MARLOWE

FROM 'PARADISE LOST'

i

Invocation

OF Man's first disobedience, and the fruit
Of that forbidden Tree, whose mortal taste
Brought death into the world, and all our woe,
With loss of Eden, till one greater Man
Restore us, and regain the blissful seat,
Sing, Heavenly Muse, that on the secret top
Of Oreb, or of Sinai, didst inspire
That shepherd, who first taught the chosen seed
In the beginning how the Heavens and Earth
Rose out of Chaos: or, if Sion hill
Delight thee more, and Siloa's brook that flowed
Fast by the oracle of God, I thence
Invoke thy aid to my adventurous song,
That with no middle flight intends to soar
Above the Aonian mount, while it pursues
Things unattempted yet in prose or rhyme.
And chiefly thou, O Spirit, that dost prefer
Before all temples the upright heart and pure,

Instruct me, for thou know'st; thou from the first
Wast present, and, with mighty wings outspread,
Dove-like sat'st brooding on the vast Abyss,
And mad'st it pregnant: what in me is dark
Illumine, what is low raise and support;
That to the highth of this great argument
I may assert Eternal Providence,
And justify the ways of God to men.

Book I, ll. 1–26.

ii

The Hosts of Satan

Then straight commands that, at the warlike sound
Of trumpets loud and clarions, be upreared
His mighty standard. That proud honour claimed
Azazel as his right, a Cherub tall:
Who forthwith from the glittering staff unfurled
The imperial ensign, which, full high advanced,
Shone like a meteor streaming to the wind,
With gems and golden lustre rich emblazed,
Seraphic arms and trophies; all the while
Sonorous metal blowing martial sounds:
At which the universal host up-sent
A shout that tore Hell's concave, and beyond
Frighted the reign of Chaos and old Night.
All in a moment through the gloom were seen
Ten thousand banners rise into the air,
With orient colours waving; with them rose
A forest huge of spears; and thronging helms
Appeared, and serried shields in thick array
Of depth immeasurable. Anon they move

– 382 –

In perfect phalanx to the Dorian mood
Of flutes and soft recorders; such as raised
To highth of noblest temper heroes old
Arming to battle, and instead of rage
Deliberate valour breathed, firm and unmoved
With dread of death to flight or foul retreat;
Nor wanting power to mitigate and swage,
With solemn touches, troubled thoughts, and chase
Anguish and doubt and fear and sorrow and pain
From mortal or immortal minds. Thus they,
Breathing united force with fixéd thought,
Moved on in silence to soft pipes that charmed
Their painful steps o'er the burnt soil; and now
Advanced in view they stand, a horrid front
Of dreadful length and dazzling arms, in guise
Of warriors old, with ordered spear and shield,
Awaiting what command their mighty Chief
Had to impose.

Book I, ll. 531–67.

iii

Chorus Angelorum

No sooner had the Almighty ceased, but—all
The multitude of Angels, with a shout
Loud as from numbers without number, sweet
As from blest voices, uttering joy—Heaven rung
With jubilee, and loud hosannas filled
The eternal regions. Lowly reverent
Towards either throne they bow, and to the ground
With solemn adoration down they cast
Their crowns inwove with amarant and gold:

Immortal amarant, a flower which once
In Paradise, fast by the Tree of Life,
Began to bloom, but soon for Man's offence
To Heaven removed, where first it grew, there grows
And flowers aloft, shading the Fount of Life,
And where the River of Bliss through midst of Heaven
Rolls o'er Elysian flowers her amber stream.
With these that never fade the Spirits elect
Bind their resplendent locks inwreathed with beams.
Now in loose garlands thick thrown off, the bright
Pavement, that like a sea of jasper shone,
Impurpled with celestial roses smiled.
Then, crowned again, their golden harps they took,
Harps ever tuned, that glittering by their side
Like quivers hung; and with preamble sweet
Of charming symphony they introduce
Their sacred song, and waken raptures high:
No voice exempt, no voice but well could join
Melodious part; such concord is in Heaven.

Book III, ll. 344–71.

JOHN MILTON

FROM 'THE GARDEN'

How vainly men themselves amaze
To win the palm, the oak, or bays,
And their uncessant labours see
Crown'd from some single herb or tree,
Whose short and narrow-vergéd shade
Does prudently their toils upbraid;
While all the flowers and trees do close
To weave the garlands of repose.

What wondrous life in this I lead!
Ripe apples drop about my head;
The luscious clusters of the vine
Upon my mouth do crush their wine;
The nectarine and curious peach
Into my hands themselves do reach;
Stumbling on melons, as I pass,
Ensnared with flowers, I fall on grass.

Meanwhile the mind from pleasure less
Withdraws into its happiness;
The mind, that ocean where each kind
Does straight its own resemblance find;
Yet it creates, transcending these,
Far other worlds, and other seas;
Annihilating all that's made
To a green thought in a green shade.

Here at the fountain's sliding foot,
Or at some fruit-tree's mossy root,
Casting the body's vest aside,
My soul into the boughs does glide;
There like a bird it sits, and sings,
Then whets, and combs its silver wings;
And, till prepared for longer flight,
Waves in its plumes the various light.

ANDREW MARVELL

FRIENDS DEPARTED

THEY are all gone into the world of light!
  And I alone sit ling'ring here;
Their very memory is fair and bright,
    And my sad thoughts doth clear.

It glows and glitters in my cloudy breast,
    Like stars upon some gloomy grove,
Or those faint beams in which this hill is drest
    After the sun's remove.

I see them walking in an air of glory,
    Whose light doth trample on my days:
My days, which are at best but dull and hoary,
    Mere glimmerings and decays.

O holy Hope! and high Humility,
    High as the heavens above!
These are your walks, and you have show'd them me,
    To kindle my cold love.

Dear, beauteous Death! the jewel of the Just,
    Shining nowhere, but in the dark;
What mysteries do lie beyond thy dust,
    Could man outlook that mark!

He that hath found some fledg'd bird's nest may know,
    At first sight, if the bird be flown;
But what fair well or grove he sings in now,
    That is to him unknown.

And yet as Angels in some brighter dreams
    Call to the soul, when man doth sleep:
So some strange thoughts transcend our wonted themes,
      And into glory peep.

If a star were confin'd into a tomb,
    Her captive flames must needs burn there;
But when the hand that lock'd her up gives room,
      She'll shine through all the sphere.

O Father of eternal life, and all
    Created glories under Thee!
Resume Thy spirit from this world of thrall
      Into true liberty.

Either disperse these mists, which blot and fill
    My pérspective still as they pass:
Or else remove me hence unto that hill,
      Where I shall need no glass.

HENRY VAUGHAN

ALEXANDER'S FEAST

An ode in honour of S. Cecilia's Day

'TWAS at the royal feast for Persia won
  By Philip's warlike son—
Aloft in awful state
The godlike hero sate
On his imperial throne;
His valiant peers were placed around,
Their brows with roses and with myrtles bound,
(So should desert in arms be crown'd);
The lovely Thais by his side
Sat like a blooming eastern bride
In flower of youth and beauty's pride:—
Happy, happy, happy pair!
None but the brave
None but the brave
None but the brave deserves the fair!

Timotheus, placed on high
Amid the tuneful choir,
With flying fingers touch'd the lyre:
The trembling notes ascend the sky
And heavenly joys inspire.
The song began from Jove
Who left his blissful seats above—
Such is the power of mighty love!
A dragon's fiery form belied the god;
Sublime on radiant spires he rode

When he to fair Olympia prest,
And while he sought her snowy breast,
Then round her slender waist he curl'd,
And stamp'd an image of himself, a sovereign of the
　　　world.
—The listening crowd admire the lofty sound!
A present deity! they shout around:
A present deity! the vaulted roofs rebound!
With ravish'd ears
The monarch hears,
Assumes the god;
Affects to nod
And seems to shake the spheres.
The praise of Bacchus then the sweet musician sung,
Of Bacchus ever fair and ever young:
The jolly god in triumph comes!
Sound the trumpets, beat the drums!
Flush'd with a purple grace
He shows his honest face;
Now give the hautboys breath. He comes! he comes!
Bacchus, ever fair and young,
Drinking joys did first ordain;
Bacchus' blessings are a treasure,
Drinking is the soldier's pleasure:
Rich the treasure,
Sweet the pleasure,
Sweet is pleasure after pain.

Soothed with the sound, the king grew vain;
Fought all his battles o'er again, 　　　　　　　　[slain!
And thrice he routed all his foes, and thrice he slew the

The master saw the madness rise,
His glowing cheeks, his ardent eyes;
And while he heaven and earth defied
Changed his hand and check'd his pride.
He chose a mournful Muse
Soft pity to infuse:
He sung Darius great and good,
By too severe a fate
Fallen, fallen, fallen, fallen,
Fallen from his high estate,
And weltering in his blood;
Deserted at his utmost need
By those his former bounty fed;
On the bare earth exposed he lies
With not a friend to close his eyes.
—With downcast looks the joyless victor sat,
Revolving in his alter'd soul
The various turns of chance below;
And now and then a sigh he stole,
And tears began to flow.

The mighty master smiled to see
That love was in the next degree;
'Twas but a kindred sound to move,
For pity melts the mind to love.
Softly sweet, in Lydian measures
Soon he soothed his soul to pleasures.
War, he sung, is toil and trouble,
Honour but an empty bubble;
Never ending, still beginning,
Fighting still, and still destroying;

If the world be worth thy winning,
Think, O think, it worth enjoying:
Lovely Thais sits beside thee,
Take the good the gods provide thee!

—The many rend the skies with loud applause;
So Love was crown'd, but Music won the cause.
The prince, unable to conceal his pain,
Gazed on the fair
Who caused his care,
And sigh'd and look'd, sigh'd and look'd **again**:
Sigh'd and look'd, and sigh'd again:
At length with love and wine at once opprest
The vanquish'd victor sunk upon her breast.

Now strike the golden lyre again:
A louder yet, and yet a louder strain!
Break his bands of sleep asunder
And rouse him like a rattling peal of thunder.
Hark! hark! the horrid sound
Has raised up his head:
As awaked from the dead
And amazed he stares around.
'Revenge, revenge,' Timotheus cries,
'See the Furies arise!
See the snakes that they rear:
How they hiss in their hair,
And the sparkles that flash from their eyes!
Behold a ghastly band,
Each a torch in his hand!

Those are Grecian ghosts, that in battle were slain
And unburied remain
Inglorious on the plain:
Give the vengeance due
To the valiant crew!
Behold how they toss their torches on high,
How they point to the Persian abodes
And glittering temples of their hostile gods.'
—The princes applaud with a furious joy:
And the King seized a flambeau with zeal to destroy;
Thais led the way
To light him to his prey,
And like another Helen, fired another Troy!

—Thus, long ago,
Ere heaving bellows learn'd to blow,
While organs yet were mute,
Timotheus, to his breathing flute
And sounding lyre
Could swell the soul to rage, or kindle soft desire.
At last divine Cecilia came,
Inventress of the vocal frame;
The sweet enthusiast from her sacred store
Enlarged the former narrow bounds,
And added length to solemn sounds,
With Nature's mother-wit, and arts unknown before.
Let old Timotheus yield the prize
Or both divide the crown;
He raised a mortal to the skies;
She drew an angel down!

JOHN DRYDEN

FROM 'THE VANITY OF HUMAN WISHES'

ON what foundation stands the warrior's pride,
  How just his hopes let Swedish Charles decide.
A frame of adamant, a soul of fire,
No dangers fright him, and no labours tire;
O'er love, o'er fear, extends his wide domain,
Unconquered lord of pleasure and of pain;
No joys to him pacific sceptres yield,
War sounds the trump, he rushes to the field.
Behold surrounding kings their powers combine,
And one capitulate, and one resign:
Peace courts his hand, but spreads her charms in vain:
'Think nothing gained,' he cries, 'till naught remain,
On Moscow's walls till Gothic standards fly,
And all be mine beneath the polar sky.'
The march begins, in military state,
And nations on his eye suspended wait;
Stern famine guards the solitary coast,
And Winter barricades the realms of frost;
He comes, nor want nor cold his course delay!—
Hide, blushing glory, hide Pultowa's day:
The vanquished hero leaves his broken bands,
And shows his miseries in distant lands;
Condemned a needy supplicant to wait,
While ladies interpose, and slaves debate.
But did not chance at length her error mend?
Did no subverted empire mark his end?
Did rival monarchs give the fatal wound?
Or hostile millions press him to the ground?

His fall was destined to a barren strand,
A petty fortress, and a dubious hand:
He left the name at which the world grew pale,
To point a moral, or adorn a tale.

SAMUEL JOHNSON

ON THE EXTINCTION OF THE VENETIAN REPUBLIC, 1802

ONCE did she hold the gorgeous east in fee;
    And was the safeguard of the west; the worth
Of Venice did not fall below her birth,
Venice, the eldest child of Liberty.
She was a maiden city, bright and free;
No guile seduced, no force could violate;
And, when she took unto herself a mate,
She must espouse the everlasting sea.
And what if she had seen those glories fade,
Those titles vanish, and that strength decay;
Yet shall some tribute of regret be paid
When her long life hath reached its final day:
Men are we, and must grieve when even the shade
Of that which once was great is passed away.

WILLIAM WORDSWORTH

KUBLA KHAN

IN Xanadu did Kubla Khan
   A stately pleasure-dome decree:
Where Alph, the sacred river, ran
Through caverns measureless to man
   Down to a sunless sea.
So twice five miles of fertile ground
With walls and towers were girdled round:
And here were gardens bright with sinuous rills,
Where blossomed many an incense-bearing tree;
And here were forests ancient as the hills,
Enfolding sunny spots of greenery.

But oh! that deep romantic chasm which slanted
Down the green hill athwart a cedarn cover!
A savage place! as holy and enchanted
As e'er beneath a waning moon was haunted
By woman wailing for her demon-lover!
And from this chasm, with ceaseless turmoil seething,
As if this Earth in fast thick pants were breathing,
A mighty fountain momently was forced:
Amid whose swift half-intermitted burst
Huge fragments vaulted like rebounding hail,
Or chaffy grain beneath the thresher's flail:
And 'mid these dancing rocks at once and ever
It flung up momently the sacred river.
Five miles meandering with a mazy motion
Through wood and dale the sacred river ran,
Then reached the caverns measureless to man,
And sank in tumult to a lifeless ocean:

And 'mid this tumult Kubla heard from far
Ancestral voices prophesying war!
  The shadow of the dome of pleasure
  Floated midway on the waves;
  Where was heard the mingled measure
  From the fountain and the caves.
It was a miracle of rare device,
A sunny pleasure-dome with caves of ice!

  A damsel with a dulcimer
  In a vision once I saw:
  It was an Abyssinian maid,
  And on her dulcimer she played,
  Singing of Mount Abora.
  Could I revive within me
  Her symphony and song,
  To such a deep delight 'twould win me
That with music loud and long,
I would build that dome in air,
That sunny dome! those caves of ice!
And all who heard should see them there,
And all should cry, Beware! Beware!
His flashing eyes, his floating hair!
Weave a circle round him thrice,
And close your eyes with holy dread,
For he on honey-dew hath fed,
And drunk the milk of Paradise.

SAMUEL TAYLOR COLERIDGE

SONG FROM 'PROMETHEUS UNBOUND'

Life of Life! thy lips enkindle
    With their love the breath between them;
And thy smiles before they dwindle
    Make the cold air fire; then screen them
In those looks, where whoso gazes
Faints, entangled in their mazes.

Child of Light! thy limbs are burning
    Through the vest which seems to hide them;
As the radiant lines of morning
    Through the clouds, ere they divide them;
And this atmosphere divinest
Shrouds thee wheresoe'er thou shinest.

Fair are others; none beholds thee,
    But thy voice sounds low and tender
Like the fairest, for it folds thee
    From the sight, that liquid splendour,
And all feel, yet see thee never,
As I feel now, lost for ever!

Lamp of Earth! where'er thou movest
    Its dim shapes are clad with brightness,
And the souls of whom thou lovest
    Walk upon the winds with lightness,
Till they fail, as I am failing,
Dizzy, lost, yet unbewailing!

PERCY BYSSHE SHELLEY

EPILOGUE TO 'PROMETHEUS UNBOUND'

THIS the day, which down the void abysm
    At the Earth-born's spell yawns for Heaven's
      despotism,
  And Conquest is dragged captive through the deep;
Love, from its awful throne of patient power
In the wise heart, from the last giddy hour
  Of dread endurance, from the slippery steep,
And narrow verge of crag-like agony, springs
And folds over the world its healing wings.

Gentleness, Virtue, Wisdom, and Endurance,
These are the seals of that most firm assurance
  Which bars the pit over Destruction's strength;
And if, with infirm hand, Eternity,
Mother of many acts and hours, should free
  The serpent that would clasp her with his length,
These are the spells by which to re-assume
An empire o'er the disentangled doom.

To suffer woes which Hope thinks infinite;
To forgive wrongs darker than death or night;
  To defy Power, which seems omnipotent;
To love, and bear; to hope till Hope creates
From its own wreck the thing it contemplates;
  Neither to change, nor falter, nor repent;
This, like thy glory, Titan, is to be
Good, great and joyous, beautiful and free;
This is alone Life, Joy, Empire, and Victory.

PERCY BYSSHE SHELLEY

THE QUESTION

I DREAM'D that, as I wander'd by the way,
  Bare Winter suddenly was changed to Spring;
And gentle odours led my steps astray,
  Mix'd with a sound of waters murmuring
Along a shelving bank of turf, which lay
  Under a copse, and hardly dared to fling
Its green arms round the bosom of the stream,
But kiss'd it and then fled, as thou mightest in dream.

There grew pied wind-flowers and violets;
  Daisies, those pearl'd Arcturi of the earth,
The constellated flower that never sets;
  Faint oxlips; tender bluebells, at whose birth
The sod scarce heaved; and that tall flower that wets—
  Like a child, half in tenderness and mirth—
Its mother's face with heaven-collected tears
When the low wind, its playmate's voice, it hears.

And in the warm hedge grew lush eglantine,
  Green cowbind and the moonlight-colour'd May,
And cherry-blossoms, and white cups whose wine
  Was the bright dew yet drain'd not by the day;
And wild roses, and ivy serpentine,
  With its dark buds and leaves wandering astray;
And flowers, azure, black, and streak'd with gold,
Fairer than any waken'd eyes behold.

And nearer to the river's trembling edge
   There grew broad flag-flowers, purple prank'd with
      white,
And starry river-buds among the sedge,
   And floating water-lilies, broad and bright,
Which lit the oak that overhung the hedge
   With moonlight beams of their own watery light;
And bulrushes, and reeds of such deep green
As soothed the dazzled eye with sober sheen.

Methought that of these visionary flowers
   I made a nosegay, bound in such a way
That the same hues which in their natural bowers
   Were mingled or opposed, the like array
Kept these imprison'd children of the Hours
   Within my hand;—and then, elate and gay,
I hasten'd to the spot whence I had come,
That I might there present it—O! to whom?

PERCY BYSSHE SHELLEY

TO ——

ONE word is too often profaned
   For me to profane it,
One feeling too falsely disdained
   For thee to disdain it.
One hope is too like despair
   For prudence to smother,
And Pity from thee more dear
   Than that from another.

I can give not what men call love,
  But wilt thou accept not
The worship the heart lifts above
  And the Heavens reject not:
The desire of the moth for the star,
  Of the night for the morrow,
The devotion to something afar
  From the sphere of our sorrow?

PERCY BYSSHE SHELLEY

TIME

UNFATHOMABLE Sea! whose waves are years,
  Ocean of Time, whose waters of deep woe
Are brackish with the salt of human tears!
  Thou shoreless flood, which in thy ebb and flow
Claspest the limits of mortality!
And sick of prey, yet howling on for more,
Vomitest thy wrecks on its inhospitable shore;
Treacherous in calm, and terrible in storm,
  Who shall put forth on thee,
    Unfathomable Sea?

PERCY BYSSHE SHELLEY

FROM 'ST. AGNES' EVE'

ST. Agnes' Eve—Ah, bitter chill it was!
  The owl, for all his feathers, was a-cold;
The hare limp'd trembling through the frozen grass,
  And silent was the flock in woolly fold:
Numb were the Beadsman's fingers, while he told
  His rosary, and while his frosted breath,
  Like pious incense from a censer old,
Seem'd taking flight for heaven, without a death,
Past the sweet Virgin's picture, while his prayer he saith.

His prayer he saith, this patient, holy man;
  Then takes his lamp, and riseth from his knees,
And back returneth, meagre, barefoot, wan,
  Along the chapel aisle by slow degrees:
The sculptur'd dead, on each side, seem to freeze,
  Emprison'd in black, purgatorial rails:
  Knights, ladies, praying in dumb orat'ries,
He passeth by; and his weak spirit fails
To think how they may ache in icy hoods and mails.

Northward he turneth through a little door,
  And scarce three steps, ere Music's golden tongue
Flatter'd to tears this aged man and poor ;
  But no—already had his deathbell rung:
The joys of all his life were said and sung:
  His was harsh penance on St. Agnes' Eve:
  Another way he went, and soon among
Rough ashes sat he for his soul's reprieve,
And all night kept awake, for sinners' sake to grieve.

JOHN KEATS

LUCIFER IN STARLIGHT

ON a starr'd night Prince Lucifer uprose.
    Tired of his dark dominion swung the fiend
  Above the rolling ball in cloud part screen'd,
Where sinners hugg'd their spectre of repose.
Poor prey to his hot fit of pride were those.
    And now upon his western wing he lean'd,
  Now his huge bulk o'er Afric's sands career'd,
Now the black planet shadow'd Arctic snows.
Soaring through wider zones that prick'd his scars
    With memory of the old revolt from Awe,
He reach'd a middle height, and at the stars,
Which are the brain of heaven, he look'd, and sank.
Around the ancient track march'd, rank on rank,
    The army of unalterable law.

GEORGE MEREDITH

FROM 'THE CITY OF DREADFUL NIGHT'

How the moon triumphs through the endless nights!
　How the stars throb and glitter as they wheel
Their thick processions of supernal lights
　　Around the blue vault obdurate as steel!
And men regard with passionate awe and yearning
The mighty marching and the golden burning,
　　And think the heavens respond to what they feel.

Boats gliding like dark shadows of a dream,
　Are glorified from vision as they pass
The quivering moonbridge on the deep black stream;
　　Cold windows kindle their dead glooms of glass
To restless crystals; cornice, dome, and column
Emerge from chaos in the splendour solemn;
　　Like faëry lakes gleam lawns of dewy grass.

With such a living light these dead eyes shine,
　These eyes of sightless heaven, that as we gaze
We read a pity, tremulous, divine,
　　Or cold majestic scorn in their pure rays:
Fond man! they are not haughty, are not tender;
There is no heart or mind in all their splendour,
　　They thread mere puppets all their marvellous maze.

If we could near them with the flight unflown,
　We should but find them worlds as sad as this,
Or suns all self-consuming like our own
　　Enringed by planet worlds as much amiss:
They wax and wane through fusion and confusion;
The spheres eternal are a grand illusion,
　　The empyrean is a void abyss.　　JAMES THOMSON

FROM THE FIRST CHORUS FROM 'ATALANTA IN CALYDON'

WHEN the hounds of spring are on winter's traces,
  The mother of months in meadow or plain
Fills the shadows and windy places
  With lisp of leaves and ripple of rain;
And the brown bright nightingale amorous
Is half assuaged for Itylus,
For the Thracian ships and the foreign faces,
  The tongueless vigil, and all the pain.

Come with bows bent and with emptying of quivers,
  Maiden most perfect, lady of light,
With a noise of winds and many rivers,
  With a clamour of waters, and with might;
Bind on thy sandals, O thou most fleet,
Over the splendour and speed of thy feet;
For the faint east quickens, the wan west shivers,
  Round the feet of the day and the feet of the night.

Where shall we find her, how shall we sing to her,
  Fold our hands round her knees, and cling?
O that man's heart were as fire and could spring to her,
  Fire, or the strength of the streams that spring!
For the stars and the winds are unto her
As raiment, as songs of the harp-player;
For the risen stars and the fallen cling to her,
  And the southwest-wind and the west-wind sing.

For winter's rains and ruins are over,
    And all the season of snows and sins;
The days dividing lover and lover,
    The light that loses, the night that wins;
And time remembered is grief forgotten,
And frosts are slain and flowers begotten,
And in green underwood and cover
    Blossom by blossom the spring begins.

ALGERNON CHARLES SWINBURNE

A FORSAKEN GARDEN

IN a coign of the cliff between lowland and highland,
    At the sea-down's edge between windward and lee,
Walled round with rocks as an inland island,
    The ghost of a garden fronts the sea,
A girdle of brushwood and thorn encloses
    The steep square slope of the blossomless bed
Where the weeds that grew green from the graves of its
    roses
        Now lie dead.

The fields fall southward, abrupt and broken,
    To the low last edge of the long lone land.
If a step should sound or a word be spoken,
    Would a ghost not rise at the strange guest's hand?
So long have the grey bare walks lain guestless,
    Through branches and briars if a man make way,
He shall find no life but the sea-wind's, restless
        Night and day.

The dense hard passage is blind and stifled
　　That crawls by a track none turn to climb
To the strait waste place that the years have rifled
　　Of all but the thorns that are touched not of time.
The thorns he spares when the rose is taken;
　　The rocks are left when he wastes the plain.
The wind that wanders, the weeds wind-shaken,
　　　　These remain.

Not a flower to be pressed of the foot that falls not;
　　As the heart of a dead man the seed-plots are dry;
From the thicket of thorns whence the nightingale calls
　　　not,
　　Could she call, there were never a rose to reply.
Over the meadows that blossom and wither
　　Rings but the note of a sea-bird's song;
Only the sun and the rain come hither
　　　　All year long.

The sun burns sere and the rain dishevels
　　One gaunt bleak blossom of scentless breath.
Only the wind here hovers and revels
　　In a round where life seems barren as death.
Here there was laughing of old, there was weeping,
　　Haply, of lovers none ever will know,
Whose eyes went seaward a hundred sleeping
　　　　Years ago.

Heart handfast in heart as they stood, 'Look thither,'
  Did he whisper? 'look forth from the flowers to the
    sea;
For the foam-flowers endure when the rose-blossoms
    wither,
  And men that love lightly may die—but we?'
And the same wind sang and the same waves whitened,
  And or ever the garden's last petals were shed,
In the lips that had whispered, the eyes that had
    lightened,
      Love was dead.

Or they loved their life through, and then went
    whither?
  And were one to the end—but what end who knows?
Love deep as the sea as a rose must wither,
  As the rose-red seaweed that mocks the rose.
Shall the dead take thought for the dead to love them?
  What love was ever as deep as a grave?
They are loveless now as the grass above them
      Or the wave.

All are at one now, roses and lovers,
  Not known of the cliffs and the fields and the sea.
Not a breath of the time that has been hovers
  In the air now soft with a summer to be.
Not a breath shall there sweeten the seasons hereafter
  Of the flowers or the lovers that laugh now or weep,
When as they that are free now of weeping and laughter
      We shall sleep.

Here death may deal not again for ever;
　　Here change may come not till all change end.
From the graves they have made they shall rise up
　　　　never,
　　Who have left nought living to ravage and rend.
Earth, stones, and thorns of the wild ground growing,
　　While the sun and the rain live, these shall be;
Till a last wind's breath upon all these blowing
　　　　Roll the sea.

Till the slow sea rise and the sheer cliff crumble,
　　Till terrace and meadow the deep gulfs drink,
Till the strength of the waves of the high tides humble
　　The fields that lessen, the rocks that shrink,
Here now in his triumph where all things falter,
　　Stretched out on the spoils that his own hand spread,
As a god self-slain on his own strange altar,
　　　　Death lies dead.

ALGERNON CHARLES SWINBURNE

THE GARDEN IN SEPTEMBER

Now thin mists temper the slow-ripening beams
Of the September sun: his golden gleams
On gaudy flowers shine, that prank the rows
Of high-grown hollyhocks, and all tall shows
That Autumn flaunteth in his bushy bowers;
Where tomtits, hanging from the drooping heads
Of giant sunflowers, peck the nutty seeds;
And in the feathery aster bees on wing
Seize and set free the honied flowers,
Till thousand stars leap with their visiting:
While ever across the path mazily flit,
Unpiloted in the sun,
The dreamy butterflies
With dazzling colours powdered and soft glooms,
White, black and crimson stripes, and peacock eyes,
Or on chance flowers sit,
With idle effort plundering one by one
The nectaries of deepest-throated blooms.

With gentle flaws the western breeze
Into the garden saileth,
Scarce here and there stirring the single trees,
For his sharpness he vaileth:
So long a comrade of the bearded corn,
Now from the stubbles whence the shocks are borne,
O'er dewy lawns he turns to stray,
As mindful of the kisses and soft play
Wherewith he enamoured the light-hearted May,
Ere he deserted her;

Lover of fragrance, and too late repents;
Nor more of heavy hyacinth now may drink,
Nor spicy pink,
Nor summer's rose, nor garnered lavender,
But the few lingering scents
Of streakéd pea, and gillyflower, and stocks
Of courtly purple, and aromatic phlox.

And at all times to hear are drowsy tones
Of dizzy flies, and humming drones,
With sudden flap of pigeon wings in the sky,
Or the wild cry
Of thirsty rooks, that scour ascare
The distant blue, to watering as they fare
With creaking pinions, or—on business bent,
If aught their ancient polity displease,—
Come gathering to their colony, and there
Settling in ragged parliament,
Some stormy council hold in the high trees.

ROBERT BRIDGES

THERE IS A HILL BESIDE THE SILVER THAMES

THERE is a hill beside the silver Thames,
  Shady with birch and beech and odorous pine:
And brilliant underfoot with thousand gems
Steeply the thickets to his floods decline.
    Straight trees in every place
    Their thick tops interlace,
And pendant branches trail their foliage fine
    Upon his watery face.

Swift from the sweltering pasturage he flows:
His stream, alert to seek the pleasant shade,
Pictures his gentle purpose, as he goes
Straight to the caverned pool his toil has made.
    His winter floods lay bare
    The stout roots in the air:
His summer streams are cool, when they have played
    Among their fibrous hair.

A rushy island guards the sacred bower,
And hides it from the meadow, where in peace
The lazy cows wrench many a scented flower,
Robbing the golden market of the bees:
    And laden barges float
    By banks of myosote;
And scented flag and golden flower-de-lys
    Delay the loitering boat.

And on this side the island, where the pool
Eddies away, are tangled mass on mass
The water-weeds, that net the fishes cool,
And scarce allow a narrow stream to pass;
  Where spreading crowfoot mars
  The drowning nenuphars,
Waving the tassels of her silken grass
  Below her silver stars.

But in the purple pool there nothing grows,
Not the white water-lily spoked with gold;
Though best she loves the hollows, and well knows
On quiet streams her broad shields to unfold:
  Yet should her roots but try
  Within these deeps to lie,
Not her long reaching stalk could ever hold
  Her waxen head so high.

Sometimes an angler comes, and drops his hook
Within its hidden depths, and 'gainst a tree
Leaning his rod, reads in some pleasant book,
Forgetting soon his pride of fishery;
  And dreams, or falls asleep,
  While curious fishes peep
About his nibbled bait, or scornfully
  Dart off and rise and leap.

And sometimes a slow figure 'neath the trees,
In ancient-fashioned smock, with tottering care
Upon a staff propping his weary knees,
May by the pathway of the forest fare:
    As from a buried day
    Across the mind will stray
Some perishing mute shadow,—and unaware
    He passeth on his way.

Else, he that wishes solitude is safe,
Whether he bathe at morning in the stream:
Or lead his love there when the hot hours chafe
The meadows, busy with a blurring steam;
    Or watch, as fades the light,
    The gibbous moon grow bright,
Until her magic rays dance in a dream,
    And glorify the night.

Where is this bower beside the silver Thames?
O pool and flowery thickets, hear my vow!
O trees of freshest foliage and straight stems,
No sharer of my secret I allow:
    Lest ere I come the while
    Strange feet your shades defile;
Or lest the burly oarsman turn his prow
    Within your guardian isle.

ROBERT BRIDGES

THE KINGDOM OF GOD

In no Strange Land

O WORLD Invisible, we view thee,
O World intangible, we touch thee,
O World unknowable, we know thee,
Inapprehensible, we clutch thee!

Does the fish soar to find the ocean,
The eagle plunge to find the air—
That we ask of the stars in motion
If they have rumour of thee there?

Not where the wheeling systems darken,
And our benumbed conceiving soars!
The drift of pinions, would we hearken,
Beats at our own clay-shuttered doors.

The angels keep their ancient places;—
Turn but a stone, and start a wing!
'Tis ye, 'tis your estrangéd faces,
That miss the many-splendoured thing.

But (when so sad thou canst not sadder)
Cry;—and upon thy so sore loss
Shall shine the traffic of Jacob's ladder
Pitched betwixt Heaven and Charing Cross.

Yea, in the night, my Soul, my daughter,
Cry,—clinging Heaven by the hems;
And lo, Christ walking on the water,
Not of Gennesareth, but Thames!

FRANCIS THOMPSON

– 415 –

TO A SNOW-FLAKE

WHAT heart could have thought you?—
Past our devisal
(O filigree petal!)
Fashioned so purely,
Fragilely, surely,
From what Paradisal
Imagineless metal,
Too costly for cost?
Who hammered you, wrought you,
From argentine vapour?—
'God was my shaper.
Passing surmisal,
He hammered, He wrought me,
From curled silver vapour,
To lust of His mind:—
Thou could'st not have thought me!
So purely, so palely,
Tinily, surely,
Mightily, frailly,
Insculped and embossed,
With His hammer of wind,
And His graver of frost.'

FRANCIS THOMPSON

TO MY GOD-CHILD

THIS labouring, vast, Tellurian galleon,
  Riding at anchor off the orient sun,
Had broken its cable, and stood out to space
Down some frore Arctic of the aerial ways:
And now, back warping from the inclement main,
Its vapourous shroudage drenched with icy rain,
It swung into its azure roads again;
When, floated on the prosperous sun-gale, you
Lit, a white halcyon auspice, 'mid our frozen crew.

To the Sun, stranger, surely you belong,
Giver of golden days and golden song;
Nor is it by an all-unhappy plan
You bear the name of me, his constant Magian.
Yet ah! from any other that it came,
Lest fated to my fate you be, as to my name.
When at the first those tidings did they bring,
My heart turned troubled at the ominous thing:
Though well may such a title him endower,
For whom a poet's prayer implores a poet's power,
The Assisian, who kept plighted faith to three,
To Song, to Sanctitude, and Poverty,
(In two alone of whom most singers prove
A fatal faithfulness of during love!)
He the sweet Sales, of whom we scarcely ken
How God he could love more, he so loved men;
The crown and crowned of Laura and Italy;
And Fletcher's fellow—from these, and not from me,
Take you your name, and take your legacy!

Or, if a right successive you declare
When worms, for ivies, intertwine my hair,
Take but this Poesy that now followeth
My clayey hest with sullen servile breath,
Made then your happy freedman by testating death.
My song I do but hold for you in trust,
I ask you but to blossom from my dust.
When you have compassed all weak I began,
Diviner poet, and ah! diviner man—
The man at feud with the perduring child
In you before song's altar nobly reconciled—
From the wise heavens I half shall smile to see
How little a world, which owned you, needed me.
If, while you keep the vigils of the night,
For your wild tears make darkness all too bright,
Some lone orb through your lonely window peeps,
As it played lover over your sweet sleeps,
Think it a golden crevice in the sky,
Which I have pierced but to behold you by!

And when, immortal mortal, droops your head,
And you, the child of deathless song, are dead;
Then, as you search with unaccustomed glance
The ranks of Paradise for my countenance,
Turn not your tread along the Uranian sod
Among the bearded counsellors of God;
For, if in Eden as on earth are we,
I sure shall keep a younger company:
Pass where beneath their rangéd gonfalons
The starry cohorts shake their shielded suns,
The dreadful mass of their enridgéd spears;

Pass where majestical the eternal peers,
The stately choice of the great Saintdom, meet—
A silvern segregation, globed complete
In sandalled shadow of the Triune feet;
Pass by where wait, young poet-wayfarer,
Your cousined clusters, emulous to share
With you the roseal lightnings burning 'mid their hair;
Pass the crystalline sea, the Lampads seven:—
Look for me in the nurseries of Heaven.

FRANCIS THOMPSON

BY THE STATUE OF KING CHARLES AT CHARING CROSS

SOMBRE and rich, the skies;
Great glooms, and starry plains.
Gently the night wind sighs;
Else a vast silence reigns.

The splendid silence clings
Around me: and around
The saddest of all kings
Crowned, and again discrowned.

Comely and calm, he rides
Hard by his own Whitehall:
Only the night wind glides:
No crowds, nor rebels, brawl.

Gone, too, his Court: and yet,
The stars his courtiers are:
Stars in their stations set;
And every wandering star.

Alone he rides, alone,
The fair and fatal king:
Dark night is all his own,
That strange and solemn thing.

Which are more full of fate:
The stars; or those sad eyes?
Which are more still and great:
Those brows; or the dark skies?

Although his whole heart yearn
In passionate tragedy:
Never was face so stern
With sweet austerity.

Vanquished in life, his death
By beauty made amends:
The passing of his breath
Won his defeated ends.

Brief life and hapless? Nay:
Through death, life grew sublime.
Speak after sentence? Yea:
And to the end of time.

Armoured he rides, his head
Bare to the stars of doom:
He triumphs now, the dead,
Beholding London's gloom.

Our wearier spirit faints,
Vexed in the world's employ:
His soul was of the saints;
And art to him was joy.

King, tried in fires of woe!
Men hunger for thy grace:
And through the night I go,
Loving thy mournful face.

Yet when the city sleeps;
When all the cries are still:
The stars and heavenly deeps
Work out a perfect will.

LIONEL JOHNSON

THE GOLDEN JOURNEY TO SAMARKAND

Prologue

WE who with songs beguile your pilgrimage
And swear that Beauty lives though lilies die,
We Poets of the proud old lineage
Who sing to find your hearts, we know not why,—

What shall we tell you? Tales, marvellous tales
   Of ships and stars and isles where good men rest,
Where nevermore the rose of sunset pales,
   And winds and shadows fall toward the West:

And there the world's first huge white-bearded kings
   In dim glades sleeping, murmur in their sleep,
And closer round their breasts the ivy clings,
   Cutting its pathway slow and red and deep.

II

And how beguile you? Death has no repose
   Warmer and deeper than that Orient sand
Which hides the beauty and bright faith of those
   Who made the Golden Journey to Samarkand.

And now they wait and whiten peaceably,
   Those conquerors, those poets, those so fair:
They know time comes not only you and I,
   But the whole world shall whiten, here or there;

When those long caravans that cross the plain
   With dauntless feet and sound of silver bells
Put forth no more for glory or for gain,
   Take no more solace from the palm-girt wells.

When the great markets by the sea shut fast
   All that calm Sunday that goes on and on:
When even lovers find their peace at last,
   And Earth is but a star, that once had shone.

Epilogue

At the Gate of the Sun, Bagdad, in olden time

The Merchants (*together*)

Away, for we are ready to a man!
  Our camels sniff the evening and are glad.
Lead on, O Master of the Caravan:
  Lead on the Merchant-Princes of Bagdad.

The Chief Draper

Have we not Indian carpets dark as wine,
  Turbans and sashes, gowns and bows and veils,
And broideries of intricate design,
  And printed hangings in enormous bales?

The Chief Grocer

We have rose-candy, we have spikenard,
  Mastic and terebinth and oil and spice,
And such sweet jams meticulously jarred
  As God's own Prophet eats in Paradise.

The Principal Jews

And we have manuscripts in peacock styles
  By Ali of Damascus; we have swords
Engraved with storks and apes and crocodiles,
  And heavy beaten necklaces, for Lords.

The Master of the Caravan

But you are nothing but a lot of Jews.

The Principal Jews

Sir, even dogs have daylight, and we pay.

The Master of the Caravan

But who are ye in rags and rotten shoes,
  You dirty-bearded, blocking up the way?

The Pilgrims

We are the Pilgrims, master; we shall go
  Always a little further: it may be
Beyond that last blue mountain barred with snow,
  Across that angry or that glimmering sea,

White on a throne or guarded in a cave
  There lives a prophet who can understand
Why men were born; but surely we are brave,
  Who make the Golden Journey to Samarkand.

The Chief Merchant

We gnaw the nail of hurry. Master, away!

One of the Women

    O turn your eyes to where your children stand.
  Is not Bagdad the beautiful? O stay!

The Merchants (*in chorus*)

    We take the Golden Road to Samarkand.

An Old Man

Have you not girls and garlands in your homes,
  Eunuchs and Syrian boys at your command?
Seek not excess: God hateth him who roams!

The Merchants (*in chorus*)
>   We make the Golden Journey to Samarkand.

A Pilgrim with a Beautiful Voice
>   Sweet to ride forth at evening from the wells
>   When shadows pass gigantic on the sand,
>   And softly through the silence beat the bells
>   Along the Golden Road to Samarkand.

A Merchant
>   We travel not for trafficking alone:
>   By hotter winds our fiery hearts are fanned:
>   For lust of knowing what should not be known
>   We make the Golden Journey to Samarkand.

The Master of the Caravan
>   Open the gate, O watchman of the night!

The Watchman
>   Ho, travellers, I open. For what land
>   Leave you the dim-moon city of delight?

The Merchants (*with a shout*)
>   We make the Golden Journey to Samarkand.

>   [*The Caravan passes through the gate*]

The Watchman (*consoling the women*)
>   What would ye, ladies? It was ever thus.
>   Men are unwise and curiously planned.

A Woman

They have their dreams, and do not think of us.

Voices of the Caravan (in the distance, singing)

We make the Golden Journey to Samarkand.

JAMES ELROY FLECKER

A SHIP, AN ISLE, A SICKLE MOON

A SHIP, an isle, a sickle moon—
  With few but with how splendid stars
The mirrors of the sea are strewn
Between their silver bars!

.   .   .   .

An isle beside an isle she lay,
The pale ship anchored in the bay,
While in the young moon's port of gold
A star-ship—as the mirrors told—
Put forth its great and lonely light
To the unreflecting Ocean, Night.
And still, a ship upon her seas,
The isle and the island cypresses
Went sailing on without the gale:
And still there moved the moon so pale,
A crescent ship without a sail!

JAMES ELROY FLECKER

THE SNARE

I HEAR a sudden cry of pain!
   There is a rabbit in a snare:
Now I hear the cry again,
   But I cannot tell from where.

But I cannot tell from where
   He is calling out for aid;
Crying on the frightened air,
   Making everything afraid.

Making everything afraid,
   Wrinkling up his little face,
As he cries again for aid;
   And I cannot find the place!

And I cannot find the place
   Where his paw is in the snare;
Little one! Oh, little one!
   I am searching everywhere.

JAMES STEPHENS

ENVOY

Go, songs, for ended is our brief, sweet play;
  Go, children of swift joy and tardy sorrow!
And some are sung, and that was yesterday,
  And some unsung, and that may be to-morrow.

Go forth; and if it be o'er stony way,
  Old joy can lend what newer grief must borrow:
And it was sweet, and that was yesterday,
  And sweet is sweet, though purchaséd with sorrow.

Go, songs, and come not back from your far way;
  And if men ask you why ye smile and sorrow,
Tell them ye grieve, for your hearts know To-day,
  Tell them ye smile, for your eyes know To-morrow.

FRANCIS THOMPSON

PART III

THE DESPAIRING LOVER

DISTRACTED with care
For Phyllis the fair,
Since nothing could move her,
Poor Damon, her lover,
Resolves in despair
No longer to languish
Nor bear so much anguish;
But, mad with his love,
To a precipice goes,
Where a leap from above
Would soon finish his woes.

When in rage he came there,
Beholding how steep
The sides did appear,
And the bottom how deep;
His torments projecting,
And sadly reflecting,
That a lover forsaken
A new love may get,
But a neck when once broken
Can never be set;
And, that he could die
Whenever he would,
But, that he could live
But as long as he could:
How grievous soever

The torment might grow,
He scorn'd to endeavour
To finish it so.
But bold, unconcern'd
At thoughts of the pain,
He calmly return'd
To his cottage again.

WILLIAM WALSH

WAITING

'O COME, O come,' the mother pray'd
    And hush'd her babe: 'let me behold
Once more thy stately form array'd
    Like autumn woods in green and gold!

'I see thy brethren come and go;
    Thy peers in stature, and in hue
Thy rivals. Some like monarchs glow
    With richest purple: some are blue

'As skies that tempt the swallow back;
    Or red as, seen o'er wintry seas,
The star of storm; or barr'd with black
    And yellow, like the April bees.

'Come they and go! I heed not, I.
    Yet others hail their advent, cling
All trustful to their side, and fly
    Safe in their gentle piloting

'To happy homes on heath or hill,
  By park or river. Still I wait
And peer into the darkness: still
  Thou com'st not—I am desolate.

'Hush! hark! I see a towering form!
  From the dim distance slowly roll'd
It rocks like lilies in a storm,
  And O, its hues are green and gold:

'It comes, it comes! Ah rest is sweet,
  And there is rest, my babe, for us!'
She ceased, as at her very feet
  Stopp'd the St. John's Wood omnibus.

CHARLES STUART CALVERLEY

ODE TO TOBACCO

Thou who, when fears attack,
  Bidst them avaunt, and Black
Care, at the horseman's back
    Perching, unseatest;
Sweet, when the morn is gray;
Sweet, when they've cleared away
Lunch; and at close of day
    Possibly sweetest:

I have a liking oid
For thee, though manifold
Stories, I know, are told,
    Not to thy credit;
How one (or two at most)
Drops make a cat a ghost—
Useless, except to roast—
    Doctors have said it:

How they who use fusees
All grow by slow degrees
Brainless as chimpanzees,
    Meagre as lizards:
Go mad, and beat their wives;
Plunge (after shocking lives)
Razors and carving knives
    Into their gizzards.

Confound such knavish tricks!
Yet know I five or six
Smokers who freely mix
    Still with their neighbours;
Jones—(who, I'm glad to say,
Asked leave of Mrs. J.)—
Daily absorbs a clay
    After his labours.

Cats may have had their goose
Cooked by tobacco-juice;
Still why deny its use
    Thoughtfully taken?
We're not as tabbies are:
Smith, take a fresh cigar!
Jones, the tobacco-jar!
    Here's to thee, Bacon![1]

CHARLES STUART CALVERLEY

THE YARN OF THE 'NANCY BELL'

'TWAS on the shores that round our coast
    From Deal to Ramsgate span,
That I found alone on a piece of stone
    An elderly naval man.

His hair was weedy, his beard was long,
    And weedy and long was he,
And I heard this wight on the shore recite,
    In a singular minor key:

'Oh, I am a cook and a captain bold,
    And the mate of the *Nancy* brig,
And a bo'sun tight, and a midshipmite,
    And the crew of the captain's gig.'

And he shook his fists and he tore his hair,
    Till I really felt afraid,
For I couldn't help thinking the man had been drinking,
    And so I simply said:

[1] A well-known Cambridge tobacconist

'Oh, elderly man, it's little I know,
  Of the duties of men of the sea,
And I'll eat my hand if I understand
  How you can possibly be

'At once a cook, and a captain bold,
  And the mate of the *Nancy* brig,
And a bo'sun tight and a midshipmite,
  And the crew of the captain's gig.'

Then he gave a hitch to his trousers, which
  Is a trick all seamen larn,
And having got rid of a thumping quid,
  He spun this painful yarn:

"'Twas in the good ship *Nancy Bell*
  That we sailed to the Indian sea,
And there on a reef we come to grief,
  Which has often occurred to me.

'And pretty nigh all o' the crew was drowned
  (There was seventy-seven o' soul)
And only ten of the *Nancy*'s men.
  Said "Here!" to the muster roll.

'There was me and the cook and the captain bold,
  And the mate of the *Nancy* brig,
And the bo'sun tight and a midshipmite,
  And the crew of the captain's gig.

'For a month we'd neither wittles nor drink,
　　Till a-hungry we did feel,
So we drawed a lot, and accordin' shot
　　The captain for our meal.

'The next lot fell to the *Nancy's* mate,
　　And a delicate dish he made;
Then our appetite with the midshipmite
　　We seven survivors stayed.

'And then we murdered the bo'sun tight,
　　And he much resembled pig;
Then we wittled free, did the cook and me,
　　On the crew of the captain's gig.

'Then only the cook and me was left,
　　And the delicate question, "Which
Of us two goes to the kettle?" arose,
　　And we argued it out as sich.

'For I loved that cook as a brother, I did,
　　And the cook he worshipped me;
But we'd both be blowed if we'd either be stowed
　　In the other chap's hold, you see.

' "I'll be eat if you dines off me," says Tom,
　　"Yes, that," says I, "you'll be,"—
"I'm boiled if I die, my friend," quoth I,
　　And "Exactly so," quoth he.

'Says he, "Dear JAMES, to murder me
  Were a foolish thing to do,
For don't you see that you can't cook *me*,
  While I can—and will—cook *you!*"

'So, he boils the water, and takes the salt
  And the pepper in portions true
(Which he never forgot) and some chopped shalot
  And some sage and parsley too.

'" Come here," says he, with a proper pride,
  Which his smiling features tell,
" 'Twill soothing be if I let you see,
  How extremely nice you'll smell."

'And he stirred it round and round and round,
  And he sniffed at the foaming froth;
When I ups with his heels, and smothers his squeals
  In the scum of the boiling broth.

'And I eat that cook in a week or less,
  And—as I eating be
The last of his chops, why I almost drops,
  For a wessel in sight I see.

        .   .   .   .

'And I never grieve, and I never smile,
  And I never larf nor play,
But I sit and croak, and a single joke
  I have—which is to say:

'Oh, I am a cook and a captain bold,
  And the mate of the *Nancy* brig,
And a bo'sun tight, and a midshipmite,
  And the crew of the captain's gig!'

W. S. GILBERT

THE WALRUS AND THE CARPENTER

THE sun was shining on the sea,
  Shining with all his might:
He did his very best to make
  The billows smooth and bright—
And this was odd, because it was
  The middle of the night.

The moon was shining sulkily,
  Because she thought the sun
Had got no business to be there
  After the day was done—
'It's very rude of him,' she said,
  'To come and spoil the fun.'

The sea was wet as wet could be,
  The sands were dry as dry.
You could not see a cloud, because
  No cloud was in the sky:
No birds were flying overhead—
  There were no birds to fly.

The Walrus and the Carpenter
  Were walking close at hand;
They wept like anything to see
  Such quantities of sand:
'If this were only cleared away,'
  They said, 'it *would* be grand.'

'If seven maids with seven mops
  Swept it for half a year,
Do you suppose,' the Walrus said,
  'That they could get it clear?'
'I doubt it,' said the Carpenter,
  And shed a bitter tear.

'O Oysters, come and walk with us!'
  The Walrus did beseech.
'A pleasant walk, a pleasant talk,
  Along the briny beach:
We cannot do with more than four,
  To give a hand to each.'

The eldest Oyster looked at him,
  But never a word he said:
The eldest Oyster winked his eye,
  And shook his heavy head—
Meaning to say he did not choose
  To leave the oyster-bed.

But four young Oysters hurried up,
    All eager for the treat:
Their coats were brushed, their faces washed,
    Their shoes were clean and neat—
And this was odd, because, you know,
    They hadn't any feet.

Four other Oysters followed them,
    And yet another four;
And thick and fast they came at last,
    And more, and more, and more—
All hopping through the frothy waves,
    And scrambling to the shore.

The Walrus and the Carpenter
    Walked on a mile or so,
And then they rested on a rock
    Conveniently low:
And all the little Oysters stood
    And waited in a row.

'The time has come,' the Walrus said,
    'To talk of many things:
Of shoes—and ships—and sealing-wax—
    Of cabbages—and kings—
And why the sea is boiling hot—
    And whether pigs have wings.'

'But wait a bit,' the Oysters cried,
  'Before we have our chat;
For some of us are out of breath,
  And all of us are fat!'
'No hurry!' said the Carpenter.
  They thanked him much for that.

'A loaf of bread,' the Walrus said,
  'Is what we chiefly need:
Pepper and vinegar besides
  Are very good indeed—
Now if you're ready, Oysters dear,
  We can begin to feed.'

'But not on us!' the Oysters cried,
  Turning a little blue.
'After such kindness, that would be
  A dismal thing to do!'
'The night is fine,' the Walrus said.
  'Do you admire the view?

'It was so kind of you to come!
  And you are very nice!'
The Carpenter said nothing but
  'Cut us another slice:
I wish you were not quite so deaf—
  I've had to ask you twice!'

'It seems a shame,' the Walrus said,
  'To play them such a trick,
After we've brought them out so far,
  And made them trot so quick!'
The Carpenter said nothing but
  'The butter's spread too thick!'

'I weep for you,' the Walrus said:
  'I deeply sympathize.'
With sobs and tears he sorted out
  Those of the largest size,
Holding his pocket-handkerchief
  Before his streaming eyes.

'O Oysters,' said the Carpenter,
  'You've had a pleasant run!
Shall we be trotting home again?'
  But answer came there none—
And this was scarcely odd, because
  They'd eaten every one.

'LEWIS CARROLL'

SOME HALLUCINATIONS

HE thought he saw an Elephant,
That practised on a fife:
He looked again, and found it was
A letter from his wife.
'At length I realize,' he said,
'The bitterness of Life!'

He thought he saw a Buffalo
Upon the chimney-piece:
He looked again, and found it was
His Sister's Husband's Niece,
'Unless you leave this house,' he said,
'I'll send for the Police!'

He thought he saw a Rattlesnake
That questioned him in Greek:
He looked again, and found it was
The Middle of Next Week.
'The one thing I regret,' he said,
'Is that it cannot speak!'

He thought he saw a Banker's Clerk
Descending from the bus:
He looked again, and found it was
A Hippopotamus:
'If this should stay to dine,' he said,
'There won't be much for us!'

'LEWIS CARROLL'

NARRATIVE MACARONIC VERSE

From THE BANKOLIDAID, *Lib. I*

CHARMER virumque I sing, Jack plumigeramque
  Arabellam.
Costermonger erat Jack Jones, asinumque agitabat;
In Covent Garden holus, sprouts vendidit asparagum-
  que.
Vendidit in Circo to the toffs Arabella the donah,
Qua Piccadilly propinquat to Shaftesbury Avenue,
  flores.

Jam Whitmonday adest; ex Newington Causeway the
  costers
Erumpunt multi celebrare their annual beano;
Quisque suum billycock habuere, et donah ferentes,
Impositique rotis, popularia carmina singing,
Happy with ale omnes—exceptis excipiendis.
Gloomily drives Jack Jones, inconsolabilis heros;
No companion habet, solus sine virgine coster.
Per Boro', per Fleet Street, per Strand, sic itur ad 'Em-
  pire';
Illinc Coventry Street peragunt in a merry procession,
Qua Piccadilly propinquat to Shaftesbury Avenue
  tandem
Gloomily Jack vehitur. Sed amet qui never amavit!

En! subito fugiunt dark thoughts; Arabella videtur.
Quum subit illius pulcherrima bloomin' imago,

- 443 -

Corde juvat Jack Jones; exclamat loudly 'What oh, there!'
Maiden ait 'Deus, ecce deus!' floresque relinquit.
Post asinum sedet illa; petunt Welsh Harp prope Hendon.

O fons Brent Reservoir! recubans sub tegmine brolli,
Brachia complexus (yum yum!) Jack kissed Arabella;
'Garn' ait illa rubens, et 'Garn' reboatur ab Echo;
Propositique tenax Jack 'Swelp me lummy, I loves yer.'
Hinc illae lacrimae; 'Jest one!' et 'Saucy, give over.'

Tempora jam mutantur, et hats; caligine cinctus
Oscula Jones iterat, mokoque immittit habenas.
Concertina manu sixteen discordia vocum
Obloquitur; cantant (ne saevi, magne policeman)
Noctem in Old Kent Road. Sic transit gloria Monday.

FRANK SIDGWICK

MULLION

My ball is in a bunch of fern,
  A jolly place to be;
An angry man is close astern—
  He waves his club at me;
Well, let him wave—the sky is blue;
Go on, old ball, we are but two—
  We *may* be down in three,
Or nine—or ten—or twenty-five—
It matters not; to be alive
  Is good enough for me.

How like the happy sheep we pass
  At random through the green,
For ever in the longest grass,
  But never in between!
There is a madness in the air;
There is a damsel over there,
  Her ball is in the brook.
Ah! what a shot—a dream, a dream!
You think it finished in the stream?
  Well, well, we'll go and look.

Who *is* this hot and hasty man
  That shouteth 'Fore!' and 'Fore!'?
We move as quickly as we can—
  Can any one do more?
Cheer up, sweet Sir, enjoy the view;
I'd take a seat if I were you,

And light your pipe again:
In quiet thought possess your soul,
For John is down a rabbit hole,
    And I am down a drain.

The ocean is a lovely sight,
    A brig is in the bay.
Was that a slice? You may be right—
    But, goodness, what a day!
Young men and maidens dot the down,
And they are beautiful and brown,
    And just as mad as me.
Sing, men and maids, for I have done
The Tenth—the Tenth!—in twenty-one,
    And John was twenty-three.

Now will I take my newest ball,
    And build a mighty tee,
And waggle once, or not at all,
    And bang it out to sea,
And hire a boat and bring it back,
And give it one terrific whack,
    And hole it out in three,
Or nine—or ten—or twenty-five—
It matters not; to be alive
At Mullion in the summer time,
At Mullion in the silly time,
    Is good enough for me.

                                    A. P. HERBERT

GOOD GNUS

WHEN cares attack and life seems black,
    How sweet it is to pot a yak,
  Or puncture hares and grizzly bears,
      And others I could mention:
But in my Animals 'Who's Who'
No name stands higher than the Gnu:
  And each new gnu that comes in view
      Receives my prompt attention.

When Afric's sun is sinking low,
And shadows wander to and fro,
  And everywhere there's in the air
      A hush that's deep and solemn;
Then is the time good men and true
With View Halloo pursue the gnu:
  (The safest spot to put your shot
      Is through the spinal column).

To take the creature by surprise
We must adopt some rude disguise,
  Although deceit is never sweet,
      And falsehoods don't attract us:
So, as with gun in hand you wait,
Remember to impersonate
  A tuft of grass, a mountain-pass,
      A kopje or a cactus.

A brief suspense, and then at last
The waiting's o'er, the vigil past:
   A careful aim. A spurt of flame.
     It's done. You've pulled the trigger,
And one more gnu, so fair and frail,
Has handed in its dinner-pail:
   (The females all are rather small,
     The males are somewhat bigger).

P. G. WODEHOUSE

INDEXES

CHRONOLOGICAL LIST OF AUTHORS

Fourteenth Century

Geoffrey Chaucer . . . . . ?1340–1400

Sixteenth Century

Edmund Spenser . . . . . ?1552–1599
Sir Walter Raleigh 1552–1618
Michael Drayton 1563–1631
William Shakespeare 1564–1616
Christopher Marlowe 1564–1593
Ben Jonson 1573–1637
John Fletcher 1579–1625
Richard Corbet 1582–1635
William Browne 1591–1643
Robert Herrick 1591–1674
James Shirley 1596–1666

Seventeenth Century

John Milton 1608–1674
John Suckling 1609–1642
Richard Lovelace 1618–1658
Andrew Marvell 1621–1678
Henry Vaughan 1622–1695
John Bunyan 1628–1688
John Dryden 1631–1700
John Wilmot, Earl of Rochester . . . 1647–1680
William Walsh 1663–1708
Alexander Pope 1688–1744

Eighteenth Century

Samuel Johnson 1709–1784
Thomas Gray 1716–1771
William Collins 1721–1759
Oliver Goldsmith 1730–1774
William Cowper 1731–1800
George Crabbe 1754–1832

William Blake	1757–1827
Robert Burns	1759–1796
James Hogg	1770–1835
William Wordsworth	1770–1850
Sir Walter Scott	1771–1832
Samuel Taylor Coleridge	1772–1834
Walter Savage Landor	1775–1864
Thomas Campbell	1777–1844
Thomas Moore	1779–1852
Thomas Love Peacock	1785–1866
George Gordon, Lord Byron	1788–1824
Richard Harris Barham	1788–1845
Charles Wolfe	1791–1823
Percy Bysshe Shelley	1792–1822
Frederick Marryat	1792–1848
John Keats	1795–1821
Thomas Hood	1799–1845

Nineteenth Century

Thomas Babington, Lord Macaulay	1800–1859
Thomas Lovell Beddoes	1803–1849
Robert Stephen Hawker	1803–1875
Henry Wadsworth Longfellow	1807–1882
Edgar Allan Poe	1809–1849
Edward Fitzgerald	1809–1883
Alfred, Lord Tennyson	1809–1892
William Makepeace Thackeray	1811–1863
Robert Browning	1812–1889
William Edmonstoune Aytoun	1813–1865
Arthur Hugh Clough	1819–1861
Charles Kingsley	1819–1875
Walt Whitman	1819–1892
Matthew Arnold	1822–1888
William Cory	1823–1892
William Allingham	1824–1889
George Meredith	1828–1909
Christina Rossetti	1830–1894
Charles Stuart Calverley	1831–1884

'Lewis Carroll'	. . . . .	1832–1898
James Thomson	. . . . .	1834–1882
William Morris	. . . . .	1834–1896
William Schwenk Gilbert	. . . .	1836–1911
Algernon Charles Swinburne	. . .	1837–1909
Austin Dobson	. . . . .	1840–1921
Robert Bridges	. . . . .	1844–1930
Robert Louis Stevenson	. . . .	1850–1894
Francis Thompson	. . . .	1859–1907
Rudyard Kipling	. . . . .	1865–1936
William Butler Yeats	. . . .	1865–
Lionel Johnson	. . . . .	1867–1902
Laurence Binyon	. . . . .	1869–
Ralph Hodgson	. . . . .	1871–
Walter De La Mare	. . . .	1873–
Gilbert Keith Chesterton	. . .	1874–
John Masefield	. . . . .	1878–
Frank Sidgwick	. . . . .	1879–
James Stephens	. . . . .	1882–
Alfred Noyes	. . . . .	1880–
Pelham Grenville Wodehouse	. .	1881–
James Elroy Flecker	. . . .	1884–1915
Rupert Brooke	. . . . .	1887–1915
Julian Henry Grenfell	. . .	1888–1915
Alan Patrick Herbert	. . . .	1890–
Giles Dixey	. . . . .	1893–
Charles Hamilton Sorley	. . .	1895–1915

INDEX OF AUTHORS

INDEX OF FIRST LINES

INDEX OF FIRST LINES

PRINTED IN GREAT BRITAIN AT THE UNIVERSITY PRESS, OXFORD
BY CHARLES BATEY, PRINTER TO THE UNIVERSITY